JOHN PRINE Beyond Words

LYRICS · CHORDS · PHOTOGRAPHS

OH BOY
RECORDS

NASHVILLE · TN

AL BUNETTA

July 12, 1942 - March 22, 2015

Thanks Al, for 40 years of friendship, support and direction.

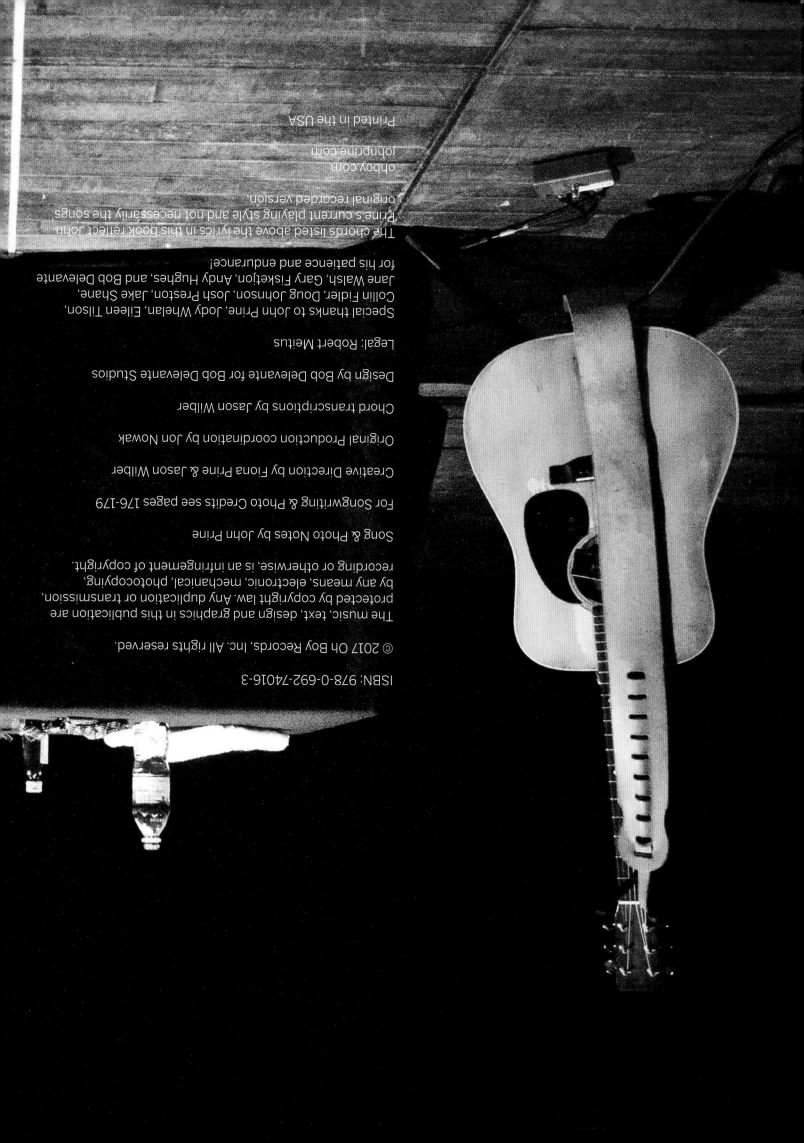

ISBN: 978-0-692-74016-3

© 2017 Oh Boy Records, Inc. All rights reserved.

Song & Photo Notes by John Prine

For Songwriting & Photo Credits see pages 176-179

Creative Direction by Fiona Prine & Jason Wilber

Original Production coordination by Jon Nowak

Chord transcriptions by Jason Wilber

Design by Bob Delevante for Bob Delevante Studios

Legal: Robert Meitus

Special thanks to John Prine, Jody Whelan, Eileen Tilson, Collin Fidler, Doug Johnson, Josh Preston, Jake Shane, Jane Walsh, Gary Fisketjon, Andy Hughes, and Bob Delevante for his patience and endurance!

The chords listed above the lyrics in this book reflect John Prine's current playing style and not necessarily the songs' original recorded version.

ohboy.com
johnprine.com

Printed in the USA

These are the steps leading down to the prison at Airdrie Hill, 'where the air smelled like snakes'. I'm the tallest one, Billy is in front, and that's our cousin Charles Allen in the middle. You didn't wanna go down any further cause there were snakes down there. My Aunt Margaret told us if you smell cucumbers get out of there, because those ain't cucumbers, they're snakes.

"Memories, they can't be boughten
 they can't be won at carnivals for free
 It took me years to get those souvenirs
 and I don't know how they slipped away from me"

- Souvenirs
  Diamonds In The Rough, 1973 , Atlantic Records

This is not just a songbook. It is a book of my lyrics with guitar chords, but it also has a lot of my personal photographs, notes, and memories.

I love photographs, particularly black and white ones, partly for the moment they capture - like loved ones no longer here, or baby pictures of my boys, who grew up too fast.

Sometimes I consider my songs to be like photographs in that they capture a moment in someone's life or a memory from my own.

You will run across some of my original work on the lyrics with lines crossed out or words scratched in with arrows. This is how I write - editing as I go along trying not to lose the original thought.

I have spent a lot of time with these old songs and photographs, or maybe it's that they've spent a lot of time with me, but I love them and I hope you will too.

After all, these songs are not just words, and these photographs are not just pictures. They are my memories and more... beyond words.

John Prine
Nashville, TN · June 2016

   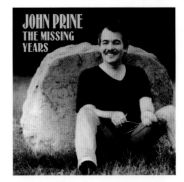

SONGS

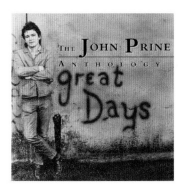

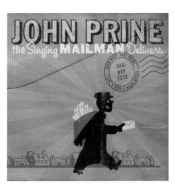

MAIN St., PARADISE, K.Y.

My grandfather lived in a one bedroom house next to the church in Paradise. This is the street that led to the dump where we'd go shoot pop bottles.

AIMLESS LOVE

Written by John Prine

```
         A                    D
He's just a small fry, a bit too gun shy
         A                          E
To have his heart touched without a glove
         A                     D
He looks at strangers as potential dangers
         A      E      A
Trying to steal his aimless love
```

```
      D                        A
Love has no mind, it can't spell unkind
                                        E
It's never seen a heart shaped like a valentine
         A                        D
For if love knew him, it'd walk up to him
         A          E        A
And introduce him to an aimless love
```

```
         A                      D
I been out walking, kinda pillow talking
         A                       E
To anyone that has the time for me
               A                         D
For there are some folks they think that love chokes
         A          E          A
It ties and keeps them from being free
```

```
      D                        A
Love has no mind, it can't spell unkind
                                        E
It's never seen a heart shaped like a valentine
         A                        D
For if love knew you, it'd walk up to you
         A               E       A
And introduce you to an aimless love
```

AIN'T HURTIN' NOBODY

Written by John Prine

Capo on 3rd Fret

A
I'm a walkin' down the street like Lucky Larue
D
Got my hand in my pocket, thinkin' 'bout you
     A   E   A
I ain't hurtin' nobody, I ain't hurtin' no one

A
There's three hundred men in the state of Tennessee
D
They're waitin' to die, they won't never be free
     A   E   A
I ain't hurtin' nobody, I ain't hurtin' no one

E   D A
Six million, seven hundred thousand and thirty-three lights on
E
You think someone could take the time to sit down
                    D A
And listen to the words of my song

A
At the beach in Indiana I was nine years old
D
I heard Little Richard singing "Tutti Frutti"

From the top of a telephone pole
      A   E   A
I wasn't hurtin' nobody, I wasn't hurtin' no one

A
There's roosters layin' chickens and chickens layin' eggs
D
Farm machinery eatin' people's arms and legs
     A   E   A
I ain't hurtin' nobody, I ain't hurtin' no one

E   D   A
Perfectly crafted popular hit songs never use the wrong rhyme
E   D A
You'd think that waitress could get my order right the first time

A
She's sittin' on the back steps just shucking that corn
D
That gal's been grinning since the day she was born
        A   E   A
She ain't hurtin' nobody, she ain't hurtin' no one

A
I used to live in Chicago where the cold wind blows
    D
I delivered more junk mail than the junkyard would hold
        A   E   A
I wasn't hurtin' nobody, I wasn't hurtin' no one

E
You can fool some of the people part of the time
                  D A
In a rock and roll song
E   D A
Fifty-million Elvis Presley fans can't be all wrong

A
I'm a walkin' down the street like Lucky Larue
D
Got my hand in my pocket baby, thinkin' 'bout you
     A   E   A
I ain't hurtin' nobody, I ain't hurtin' no one

I started taking a few lessons again, after the army, at Old Town School of Folk Music. The Fifth Peg was across the street. One night I went over there for a beer and got the courage to get up on stage.

NAME: _JOHN E. PRINE_ DATE: _2-13-69_

ADDRESS: _902 N. 19TH AVE_

CITY, ZIP CODE: _MELROSE PK, ILL._

TELEPHONE: _344-6406_

OCCUPATION: (if student, school and grade)
POSTMAN AGE: _22_

INSTRUMENT: (check one)

GUITAR ☒ *adv 2-13-69*

BANJO ☐

OTHER: _____

SEP 26 1963

pd 10/17
OCT 17 1963
OCT 24 1963
OCT 31 1963
NOV 4 1963
NOV 11 1963

pd 11/18
NOV 18 1963
DEC 2 1963
DEC 9 1963
DEC 23 1963
JAN 9 1964

pd 1/16/64
JAN 16 1964
JAN 23 1964
JAN 30 1964
FEB 6 '64
FEB 13 1964

pd 2/2/64
FEB 20 1964
MAR 5 1964
MAR 12 1964
MAR 19 1964

pd 3/26/64
MAR
APR
APR 9 1964
APR 16 1964
APR 23 1964

pd 4/30/64
APR 30 1964
MAY 7 1964
MAY 14 1964
MAY 21 1964
MAY 28 1964

pd 6/12
JUN 4 1964
JUN 11 1964
JUN 18 1964
JUL 2 1964
JUL 9 1964

JUL 16 1964
JUL 23 1964

pd 9/17
SEP 17 1964
SEP 24 1964
OCT 1 1964
OCT 8 1964
OCT 15 1964

pd 16.00 10/21
OCT 22 1964
OCT 29 1964
NOV 5 1964
NOV 12 1964
DEC 3 1964

pd 1/7/65
DEC 10 1964
JAN 7 1965
JAN 12 1965
JAN 21 1965
JAN 28 1965

pd 16.00 3/4
FEB 4 1965
MAR 4 1965
MAR 11 1965
MAR 18 1965
MAR 25 1965

pd 4/1
APR 15 1965
APR 22 1965
APR 29 1965
extend 2
JUL 15 1965

pd 15.00 9/16

SEP 16 1965
SEP 23 1965
SEP 30 1965
OCT 7 1965
Oct. 14 '65

pd 10/28
Oct. 21 '65
OCT 28 1965
NOV 4 1965
NOV 18 1965
JAN 6 1966

John Prine 44.05

ALL THE BEST

Written by John Prine

Capo on 5th Fret

```
G              C  G
I wish you love
             C  G
And happiness
           D7        G
I guess I wish you all the best

G              C  G
I wish you don't
         C  G
Do like I do
                    D7          G
And ever fall in love with someone like you
```

```
G         C         G
Cause if you fell just like I did
          G                        D7
You'd probably walk around the block like a little kid
          G   C  G
But kids don't know
                C  G
They can only guess
            D7          G
How hard it is to wish you happiness
```

```
G              C  G
I guess that love
             C  G
Is like a Christmas card
           D7              G
You decorate a tree, you throw it in the yard

G              C  G
It decays and dies
             C  G
And the snowmen melt
              D7          G
Well I once knew love, I knew how love felt
```

```
G         C         G
Yeah I knew love, love knew me
                              D7
And when I walked, love walked with me
            G   C  G
And I got no hate
              C  G
And I got no pride
             D7              G
Well I got so much love that I cannot hide
             D7              G
Yeah I got so much love that I cannot hide
```

```
G              C  G
Say you drive a Chevy
           C  G
Say you drive a Ford
                    D7              G
You say you drive around the town 'til you just get bored
```

```
G                  C  G
And then you change your mind
              C  G
For something else to do
             D7              G
And your heart gets bored with your mind and it changes you
```

```
G         C         G
Well it's a doggone shame and it's an awful mess
          D7          G
I wish you love, I wish you happiness
          D7          G
I wish you love, I wish you happiness
          D7          G
I guess I wish you all the best
```

18

THE SINS of MEMPHISTO
(IN LIPSTICK)

1. HE PUT HIS PICTURE IN A
PICTURE SHOW

2. ALL THE BEST

3. ITS A BIG OLD GOOFY WORLD

4. THE THIRD OF JULY

5. EVERYTHING IS COOL

6. GREAT RAIN M-CAMPBEL

7. EVERYBODY WANTS TO FEEL
LIKE YOU

8. WAY BACK THEN

9. YOU GOT GOLD

10. THE SINS OF MEMPHIST

11. TAKE A LOOK AT MY
HEART

12. JESUS; THE MISSING
YEARS *
* A MINE SERIES

ANGEL FROM MONTGOMERY

Written by John Prine

```
G          C       G           C
I am an old woman, named after my mother
G          C       D           G
My old man is another child that's grown old
           C        G          C
If dreams were lightning and thunder were desire
G                   C         D         G
This old house would have burnt down a long time ago
```

```
G         F          C              G
Make me an angel that flies from Montgomery
          F          C       G
Make me a poster of an old rodeo
          F          C           G
Just give me one thing that I can hold on to
              C           D         G
To believe in this living is just a hard way to go
```

```
G          C       G           C
When I was a young girl, well I had me a cowboy
G               C          D          G
He weren't much to look at, just a free rambling man
           C        G          C
But that was a long time and no matter how I try
G          C       D           G
The years just flow by like a broken down dam
```

```
G         F          C              G
Make me an angel that flies from Montgomery
          F          C       G
Make me a poster of an old rodeo
          F          C           G
Just give me one thing that I can hold on to
              C           D         G
To believe in this living is just a hard way to go
```

```
G            C       G              C
There's flies in the kitchen, I can hear 'em there buzzing
G          C          D         G
And I ain't done nothing since I woke up today
              C      G            C
How the hell can a person go to work in the morning
G             C            D        G
And come home in the evening and have nothing to say
```

```
G         F          C              G
Make me an angel that flies from Montgomery
          F          C       G
Make me a poster of an old rodeo
          F          C           G
Just give me one thing that I can hold on to
              C           D         G
To believe in this living is just a hard way to go
```

I used to doodle a lot as I wrote, and usually edit as I go. These first few lines are how I got into the opening verse of Angel from Montgomery. I think laterally, you know?

backroad
~~side~~ street rambling ~~stoplite~~ ~~highway~~ gambling
~~Too~~ 1^{50} many chances nowhere to go
seems forever heavy feathers ~~float~~ float
    like arrows

I am an old woman
named for my mother
My old man is ~~another~~ another ~~child~~
child, ~~Kid~~ thats grown old

If dreams were lighting
and thunder was desire
this ~~ol'd~~ house would have burnt
                    down
a long time ago

Make me an ~~■■~~ angel that
        flies ~~from~~ from Montgomery
make me a poster of an old rodeo
just Give me ~~one~~ ~~something~~ that I can
~~relivin' along this living~~   hold on to
This living is a hard way to go

AUTOMOBILE

Written by John Prine

E
February morning, my car won't start today
I turned the key at eight o' three and the battery passed away
Inside of my automobile, I want my automobile, I want my automobile
        B   E
I want to drive it all around this world

E
Bride's getting married in the springtime, widow's getting married in the fall
I got married in high school or I wouldn't of got married at all
I'd be driving my automobile, be driving my automobile,be driving my automobile
        B   E
I want to drive it all around this world

E
Everybody said to the new groom, "Groom, what ya gonna be"
I said, "I'm gonna be a symphony just as soon as I find a key
To my automobile," I want my automobile, I want my automobile
B   E
All around this world

E
Columbus sailed the ocean, Moses parted the sea
Dolores left me yesterday, well I think she took the key
To my automobile, I want my automobile, I want my automobile
        B   E
Want to drive it all around this world

E
Now I held a little bitty baby, I held a woman all night
Whenever I get the hiccups, I hold my breath 'til my head gets light
Then I drive my automobile, yeah I drive my automobile, I drive my automobile
        B   E
I want to drive it all around this world

E
February morning, my car won't start today
I turned the key at eight o' three and the battery passed away
Inside of my automobile, I want my automobile, I want my automobile
        B   E
I want to drive it all around this world

My '51 Ford. One of my buddies was a good photographer. I wanted a good picture of my car. I don't know what you would call that hair style. The wind was blowing, hopefully.

BLUE UMBRELLA

Feelings ARE STRANGE ESPECIALLY
WHEN THEY COME TRUE

And I had a feeling that you'd be leaving soon
So I tried to rearrange all my emotions
But It seems the same no matter what I

CHORUS
And Blue Umbrella rest upon my shoulder
Hide the pain while the rain makes up
my mind
Well my feet are wet from thinking this
over
and It's been so long since I felt them
sunshine

Just give me one good reason
And I promise I won't ask you anymore
Just give me one extra season
So I can figure out the other four

BLUE UMBRELLA

Written by John Prine

C   F   C
Feelings are strange, especially when they come true
                 G   C
And I had a feeling that you'd be leaving soon
     F   C
So I tried to rearrange all my emotions
               G   C
But it seems the same no matter what I do

C   F   C
Blue umbrella, rest upon my shoulder
                 G   C
Hide the pain while the rain makes up my mind
                F   C
Well my feet are wet from thinking this thing over
                 F   G
And it's been so long since I felt the warm sunshine
F   G   C
Just give me one good reason
    F   G   C
And I promise I won't ask you anymore
F   G   C
Just give me one extra season
          G   C
So I can figure out the other four

C   F   C
Daytime makes me wonder why you left me
                 G   C
Nighttime makes me wonder what I said
             F   C
"Next time" are the words I'd like to plan on
               G   C
But "last time" was the only thing you said

C   F   C
Blue umbrella, rest upon my shoulder
                 G   C
Hide the pain while the rain makes up my mind
                F   C
Well my feet are wet from thinking this thing over
                 F   G
And it's been so long since I felt the warm sunshine
F   G   C
Just give me one good reason
    F   G   C
And I promise I won't ask you anymore
F   G   C
Just give me one extra season
          G   C
So I can figure out the other four

Illegal smile? Beer buzz? Or just pure adrenaline?

BRUISED ORANGE (CHAIN OF SORROW)

Written by John Prine

A
My heart's in the ice house come hill or come valley
   D
Like a long ago Sunday when I walked through the alley
  A   E
On a cold winter's morning to a church house
         A
Just to shovel some snow

A
I heard sirens on the train track howl naked getting nuder
  D
An altar boy's been hit by a local commuter
      A   E
Just from walking with his back turned to the train
         A
That was coming so slow

     D
You can gaze out the window get mad and get madder
     A
Throw your hands in the air, say, "What does it matter"
  E   A
But it don't do no good to get angry so help me I know
  D
For a heart stained in anger grows weak and grows bitter
 A
You become your own prisoner as you watch yourself sit there
    E   A
Wrapped up in a trap of your very own chain of sorrow

     A
I been brought down to zero, pulled out and put back there
 D
I sat on a park bench, kissed the girl with the black hair
   A   E
And my head shouted down to my heart
       A
"You better look out below"

A
Hey it ain't such a long drop, don't stammer don't stutter
   D
From the diamonds in the sidewalk to the dirt in the gutter
   A   E
And you carry those bruises to remind you
    A
Wherever you go

   D
You can gaze out the window get mad and get madder
    A
Throw your hands in the air, say, "What does it matter"
  E   A
But it don't do no good to get angry so help me I know
  D
For a heart stained in anger grows weak and grows bitter
  A
You become your own prisoner as you watch yourself sit there
   E   A
Wrapped up in a trap of your very own chain of sorrow

A
My heart's in the ice house come hill or come valley
   D
Like a long ago Sunday when I walked through the alley
  A   E
On a cold winter's morning to a church house
        A
Just to shovel some snow

A
I heard sirens on the train track howl naked getting nuder
  D
An altar boy's been hit by a local commuter
     A   E
Just from walking with his back turned to the train
        A
That was coming so slow

    D
You can gaze out the window get mad and get madder
     A
Throw your hands in the air, say, "What does it matter"
  E   A
But it don't do no good to get angry so help me I know
  D
For a heart stained in anger grows weak and grows bitter
 A
You become your own prisoner as you watch yourself sit there
    E   A
Wrapped up in a trap of your very own chain of sorrow

Someones in my Chimney
And it sure ain't Santa Clause

You can gaze out the window
get mad and get madder
Throw your hands in the air
and say what does it matter
But it don't do no good to get angry
for help me, I know
For a heart staired in anger
grows weak and grows bitter
come ~~hell or high~~ water you'll
~~you'll become your own prisoner~~
and watch yourself sit there
wrapped up in your own ~~in~~
          very own
chains of sorrow

CHRISTMAS IN PRISON

Written by John Prine

G   C
It was Christmas in prison and the food was real good
       G   D
We had turkey and pistols carved out of wood
      G   C
And I dream of her always even when I don't dream
      G   D   G
Her name's on my tongue and her blood's in my stream

D   C   G
Wait awhile eternity
C   G   D
Old Mother Nature's got nothing on me
G   C
Come to me, run to me, come to me now
**   G   D   G**
We're rolling, my sweetheart, we're flowing, by God

       G   C
She reminds me of a chess game with someone I admire
      G   D
Or a picnic in the rain after a prairie fire
      G   C
Her heart is as big as this whole goddamn jail
        G   D   G
And she's sweeter than saccharine at a drug store sale

D   C   G
Wait awhile eternity
C   G   D
Old Mother Nature's got nothing on me
G   C
Come to me, run to me, come to me now
**   G   D   G**
We're rolling, my sweetheart, we're flowing, by God

       G   C
The searchlight in the big yard swings around with the gun
      G   D
And spotlights the snowflakes like the dust in the sun
      G   C
It's Christmas in prison, there'll be music tonight
     G   D   G
I'll probably get homesick, I love you, goodnight

D   C   G
Wait awhile eternity
C   G   D
Old Mother Nature's got nothing on me
G   C
Come to me, run to me, come to me now
**   G   D   G**
We're rolling, my sweetheart, we're flowing, by God

AFTER DARK

The Star & News
Washington, D.C
11/9/72

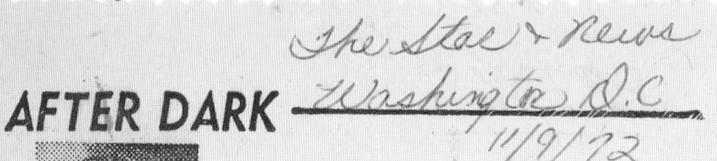

Entertaining As a Dog Bite

By JOHN SEGRAVES

So much seems out of joint in District entertainment circles these days. A few examples. Meg Christian, a folk guitarist-vocalist of unquestioned talent, barely is getting enough work to keep her instrument tuned. Mort Sahl, one of the more brilliant political humorists to step on a stage for decades, barely had enough for a quorum during his recent engagement at the Cellar Door.

Then the Georgetown club merely announces that John Prine, a former Chicago mailman turned composer-folk singer whose melodies are so similar they can barely be told apart and whose voice is like poor-quality sandpaper, has been booked and every show

denim jacket and smiles a lot. The jammed club titters and squeals at everything he says. One would imagine a small belch would bring down the house.

His all self-written, are primarily "downers," to use the contemporary vernacular. His biggie of the moment is "Sam Stone" about a Vietnam veteran hooked on heroin. Another is about the elderly whom no one cares about and are sitting around waiting to die.

Oh yes, there's that good old trio of realism, pathos and poignancy in Prine's songs. There's also enough gloom and despair to give soap-opera scripters enough ammunition for a new series. In the main, he's about as entertaining as a dog bite.

COMMON SENSE

Written by John Prine

G   Am
You can't live together, you can't live alone
D   G
Considering the weather, oh my how you've grown
                               Am
From the men in the factories to the wild kangaroo
          D
Like those birds of a feather, they're gathering together
                    G
And feeling exactly like you

G   C
They got mesmerized by lullabies and limbo danced in pairs
                  Am
Please lock that door
         D
It don't make much sense, that common sense
                  G
Don't make no sense no more

       C   D   G
Just between you and me
  C G   D   G
It's like pulling when you ought to be shoving
C   G   D   G
Like a nun with her head in the oven
C   G   D   G
Please don't tell me that this really wasn't nothing

G   Am
One of these days, one of these nights
D   G
You'll take off your hat and they'll read you your rights
                             Am
You'll wanna get high every time you feel low
          D
Hey Queen Isabella, stay away from that fella
                       G
He'll just get you into trouble you know

G   Am
But they came here by boat and they came here by plane
D   G
They blistered their hands and they burned out their brain
                             Am
All dreaming a dream that'll never come true
          D
Hey don't give me no trouble or I'll call up my double
                       G
We'll play piggy-in-the-middle with you

G   C
You'll get mesmerized by alibis and limbo dance in pairs
                  Am
Please lock that door
         D
It don't make much sense, that common sense
                  G
Don't make no sense no more

Me and Al listening to Diamonds in the Rough masters. We did the whole thing in 3 days in New York at Atlantic Studio. As our wonderful producer, Arif Mardin, said, "It cost $6800 including beer."

It was weird, going from zero to the speed of sound. The hardest thing was to accept the compliments - to go from nothing to "You're a genius." How many times can you shake your head and shuffle your feet? I was playing with an erector set and inventing the atom bomb by mistake.

CRAZY AS A LOON

Written by John Prine and Pat McLaughlin

```
A               D                    A
Back before I was a movie star, straight off of the farm
              E                          A
I had a picture of another man's wife tattooed on my arm
                D                        A
With a pack of Camel cigarettes in the sleeve of my tee shirt
             E                          A
Heading out to Hollywood just to have my feelings hurt
                D                    A
That town will make you crazy, just give it a little time
                      E                        A
You'll be walking 'round in circles, down at Hollywood and Vine
                D                        A
You'll be waiting on a phone call at the wrong end of a broom
                        E            A
Yes that town will make you crazy, crazy as a loon


A  .            D                    A
So I headed down to Nashville to become a country star
                     E                        A
Every night you'd find me hanging at every honky tonk and bar
              D                        A
Pretty soon I met a woman, pretty soon she done me wrong
                E                      A
Pretty soon my life got sadder than any country song
                D                    A
That town will make you crazy, just give it a little time
                      E                        A
You'll be walking 'round in circles, looking for that country rhyme
              D                          A
You'll be waiting on a phone call, at the wrong end of a broom
                        E            A
Yeah that town will make you crazy, crazy as a loon


A            D                    A
So I gathered up my savvy, bought myself a business suit
                E                            A
I headed up to New York City, where a man can make some loot
              D                        A
I got hired Monday morning, downsized that afternoon
                E                      A
Overcome with grief that evening, now I'm crazy as a loon
            D                        A
So I'm up here in the Northwoods, just staring at a lake
                E                        A
Wondering just exactly how much they think a man can take
            D                            A
I eat fish to pass the time away, 'neath this blue Canadian moon
                  E              A
This old world has made me crazy, crazy as a loon
```

CROOKED PIECE OF TIME

Written by John Prine

```
G                          C      G/B      A
Things got rough, things got tough, things got harder than hard
D                          C   D   G
We were just trying to make a living in our backyard
                           C      G/B      A
We were born too late, died too soon, anxiety's a terrible crime
      D                                 C      D      G
If you can't come now, don't come at all, cause it's a crooked piece of time
```

```
   G                              C  G/B  A
It's a crooked piece of time that we live in
D             C        D      G
All in all and all in all, it's a crooked piece of time
```

```
G              C G/B  A
Yesterday morning an ill wind came
D          C      D     G
Blew your picture right out of the picture frame
                       C      G/B      A
Even blew the candle out from underneath the flame
D             C D   G
Yesterday morning an ill wind came
```

```
   G                              C  G/B  A
It's a crooked piece of time that we live in
D             C        D      G
All in all and all in all, it's a crooked piece of time
```

```
G                          C      G/B      A
Things got rough, things got tough, things got harder than hard
D                          C  D  G
We were just trying to make a living in our backyard
                              C      G/B      A
We were born too late, died too soon, anxiety's a terrible crime
      D                                 C    D      G
If you can't come now, don't come at all, cause it's a crooked piece of time
```

```
   G                              C  G/B  A
It's a crooked piece of time that we live in
D             C        D      G
All in all and all in all, it's a crooked piece of time
```

I hate my hair in all of these photos, but if I had it now, I could put it on top of my head.

DEAR ABBY

Written by John Prine

Capo on 4th Fret

```
      G                    C        G
Dear Abby, Dear Abby, my feet are too long
                        A7         D
My hair's falling out and my rights are all wrong
      G                        C        G
My friends they all tell me that I've no friends at all
                             D        G
Won't you write me a letter, won't you give me a call
C    D    G
Signed, 'Bewildered'
```

```
      G                  C          G
Bewildered, Bewildered, you have no complaint
                            A7          D
You are what your are and you ain't what you ain't
      G               C        G
So listen up Buster and listen up good
                         D            G
Stop wishing for bad luck and knocking on wood
```

```
      G                    C          G
Dear Abby, Dear Abby, my fountain pen leaks
                        A7         D
My wife hollers at me and my kids are all freaks
      G                    C            G
Every side I get up on is the wrong side of bed
                       D          G
If it weren't so expensive I'd wish I were dead
C    D    G
Signed, 'Unhappy'
```

```
      G              C          G
Unhappy, Unhappy, you have no complaint
                          A7           D
You are what your are and you ain't what you ain't
      G               C        G
So listen up Buster and listen up good
                         D            G
Stop wishing for bad luck and knocking on wood
```

```
      G                    C         G
Dear Abby, Dear Abby, you won't believe this
                              A7    D
But my stomach makes noises whenever I kiss
      G                    C      G
My girlfriend tells me it's all in my head
                         D          G
But my stomach tells me to write you instead
C    D    G
Signed, 'Noisemaker'
```

```
      G                  C          G
Noisemaker, Noisemaker, you have no complaint
                            A7          D
You are what your are and you ain't what you ain't
      G               C        G
So listen up Buster and listen up good
                         D            G
Stop wishing for bad luck and knocking on wood
```

```
      G                    C        G
Dear Abby, Dear Abby, well I never thought
                              A7     D
That me and my girlfriend would ever get caught
         G                      C           G
We were sitting in the back seat just shooting the breeze
                               D          G
With her hair up in curlers and her pants to her knees
C    D    G
Signed, 'Just Married'
```

```
      G                      C           G
Just Married, Just Married, you have no complaint
                            A7           D
You are what your are and you ain't what you ain't
      G               C        G
So listen up Buster and listen up good
                         D            G
Stop wishing for bad luck and knocking on wood
C    D    G
Signed, 'Dear Abby'
```

Stomach Story Familia[r]

By ABIGAIL VAN BUREN

DEAR ABBY: I do believe you've been had.

Your column in the San Francisco Chronicle ran a letter from a man who signed himself "Noisemaker." Seems he had a noisy stomach problem every time he kissed his girlfriend.

When I read the column, as I always do, that particular letter seemed very familiar to me. I had heard it before. Let me quote to you the third stanza of the song "Dear Abby," by John Prine:

"Dear Abby, Dear Abby ...
"You won't believe this
"But my stomach makes noises
"Whenever I kiss.
"My girlfriend tells me
"It's all in my head
"But my stomach tells me
"To write you instead.
"Signed Noisemaker."

I thought for sure that you would have heard the song as, after all, it is about you. However, your reply to "Noisemaker" was a serious one. Were you really had, Abby, or is the joke on us? Sign me...**PRINE (AND ABBY) FAN IN PALO ALTO**

DEAR FAN: I was had. And if there's a joke here, it's on me. I heard the song "Dear Abby" when it first came out about 12 years ago, but I was not familiar with the lyrics.

Thank you, and the hundreds of other Prine (and Abby) fans who wrote to call this to my attention. I also received about 50 cassettes of that catchy song that caught me with my guard down.

* * *

DEAR ABBY: I have been married for five months and have a wonderful marriage, except for one small problem. My husband never answers me when I talk to him.

He doesn't even ask me to repeat what I've said. He just sits there as though I haven't even opened my mouth.

I know this isn't an uncommon problem because my mother says my father has been doing the same thing to

---

and neither is my husba[n]
TO THE WALL

DEAR TALKING: It's
ers see us, but take a goo[d]
rattle on and on until y[ou]
to tune her out? Is her c[onversation]
boring?

If she's a chatterbox
you're like your mother [or]
father.

DEAR ABBY: About f[ans who comment]
ed on how disgusting it w[as]
ally chewing tobacco, but
ball players chewed toba[cco]
ternative, so here goes:

Baseball is a dry, hot a[nd dusty game, and their]
mouths get dry. If they d[on't]
down, and their game is
er eats too much before a
creases thirst.

About 20 years ago, wh[en I]
used to buy something ca[lled]
round balls and was sold i[n]

If you can find out if sp[ecial]
your friend for life and
HURLEY IN PORTLAN[D]

DEAR MR. HURLEY:
you, you could be stuck

(Do you hate to write
what to say? Thank-you [note]
lations, how to decline a
write an interesting lette[r]
"How to Write Letters fo[r]
and address clearly prin[ted]
for $2.50 (this includes

DONALD AND LYDIA
Written by John Prine

Capo on 5th Fret

```
G                      C       G
Small town, bright lights, Saturday night
                    A7        D
Pinballs and pool halls are flashing their lights
      G                              C      G
Making change behind the counter in a penny arcade
                         D       G
Sat the fat girl daughter of Virginia and Ray
```

(Spoken) Lydia

```
G        C           G
Lydia hid her thoughts like a cat
              A7        D
Behind her small eyes sunk deep in her fat
      G                     C      G
She read Romance Magazine up in her room
                         D       G
And felt just like Sunday on Saturday afternoon
```

```
     C                G
But dreaming just comes natural
     D              G
Like the first breath from a baby
     C              G
Like sunshine feeding daisies
          D                  G
Like the love hidden deep in your heart
```

```
G                       C       G
Bunk beds, shaved heads, Saturday night
                    A7        D
A warehouse of strangers with sixty watt lights
G                         C       G
Staring through the ceiling, just wanting to be
                    D       G
Lay one of too many, a young P.F.C.
```

(Spoken) Donald

```
        G                         C      G
There were spaces between Donald and whatever he said
                    A7        D
Strangers had forced him to live in his head
      G                     C      G
He envisioned the details of romantic scenes
                            D       G
After midnight in the stillness of the barracks' latrine
```

```
C                    G
But dreaming just comes natural
          D                  G
Like the first breath from a baby
     C              G
Like sunshine feeding daisies
          D                  G
Like the love hidden deep in your heart
```

```
G        C           G
Hot love, cold love, no love at all
                    A7         D
A portrait of guilt is hung on the wall
G                          C      G
Nothing is wrong and nothing is right
                     D          G
Donald and Lydia made love that night
```

(Spoken) Love

```
        G                         C      G
They made love in the mountains, they made love in the streams
                              A7        D
They made love in the valleys, they made love in their dreams
        G                          C       G
But when they were finished there was nothing to say
                         D       G
Cause mostly they made love from ten miles away
```

```
     C                G
But dreaming just comes natural
     D              G
Like the first breath from a baby
     C              G
Like sunshine feeding daisies
          D                  G
Like the love hidden deep in your heart
```

EVERYTHING IS COOL

Written by John Prine

Capo on 1st Fret

```
E              A             E
Everything is cool, everything's okay
                      B7                    E
Why just before last Christmas, my baby went away
                          A                      E
Across the sea to an island, where the bridges brightly burn
                B7                    E
So far away from my land, the valley of the unconcerned


E                       A                  E
I was walking down the road man, just looking at my shoes
                          B7                    E
When God sent me an angel, just to chase away my blues
                        A                          E
I saw a hundred thousand blackbirds, just flying through the sky
                            B7                          E
And they seemed to form a teardrop from a black haired angel's eye
                  A                      E
That tear fell all around me, and it washed my sins away
                  B7              E
Now everything is cool, everything's okay


E               A             E
Everything is cool, everything's okay
                    B7                      E
Why just before last Christmas, my baby went away
                    A                        E
And I find it real surprising for myself to hear me say
                    B7              E
That everything is cool, everything's okay
                B7              E
Everything is cool, everything's okay
                          B7                      E
Why it was just before last Christmas, my baby went away
```

FAR FROM ME

Written by John Prine

Capo on 5th Fret

```
        G          C                    D
As the cafe was closing on a warm summer night
   C           D           G
And Cathy was cleaning the spoons
        C            G
The radio played the "Hit Parade"
      A7                   D
And I hummed along with the tune
        C              G
She asked me to change the station
             C              D
Said the song just drove her insane
     G                  C
But it weren't just the music playing
        D                  G
It was me she was trying to blame
```

```
          C             G
And the sky is black and still now
        C                   D
On the hill where the angels sing
        C                   G
Ain't it funny how an old broken bottle
              D          G
Looks just like a diamond ring
           C  D    G
But it's far, far from me
```

```
        G            C                     D
Well I leaned on my left leg in the parking lot dirt
       C         D          G
And Cathy was closing the lights
      C               G
A June bug flew from the warmth he once knew
        A7                   D
And I wished for once I weren't right
        C              G
Why we used to laugh together
             C              D
And we'd dance to any old song
            G                  C
Well you know, she still laughs with me
           D                G
But she waits just a second too long
```

```
          C             G
And the sky is black and still now
        C                   D
On the hill where the angels sing
        C                   G
Ain't it funny how an old broken bottle
              D          G
Looks just like a diamond ring
           C  D    G
But it's far, far from me
```

```
        G            C                       D
Well I started the engine and I gave it some gas
       C          D          G
And Cathy was closing her purse
      C                        G
Well we hadn't gone far in my beat up old car
       A7                  D
And I was prepared for the worst
C                      G
"Will you still see me tomorrow"
C                D
"No, I got too much to do"
        G                  C
Well a question ain't really a question
    D                  G
If you know the answer too
```

```
          C             G
And the sky is black and still now
        C                   D
On the hill where the angels sing
        C                   G
Ain't it funny how an old broken bottle
              D          G
Looks just like a diamond ring
           C  D    G
But it's far, far from me
```

The original title was "The Closing of the Cafe". I was going out with a waitress when I was 15 years old and she broke my heart. The picture I paint in the song is more like a cafe out along a dusty highway. In the song I have a car but I didn't have a car when I was dating her. That's why I lost her. I lost her to a guy with a '58 Impala.

FAR FROM ME

~~THE CLOSING OF THE CAFE~~

by (c) john prine 1971

AS THE CAFE WAS CLOSING
ON A WARM SUMMER NITE
AND CATHY WAS CLEANING THE SPOONS
THE RADIO PLAYED THE HIT PARADE
AND I HUMMED ALONG WITH THE TUNE
SHE ASKED ME TO CHANGE THE STATION
SAID THE SONG JUST DROVE HER INSANE
BUT IT WEREN'T JUST THE MUSIC A PLAYING
IT WAS ME SHE WAS TRYING TO BLAME

        CHORUS

AND THE SKY IS BLACK AND STILLXZ NOW
ON THE HILL WHERE THE ANGELS SING
AIN'T IT FUNNY HOW AN OLD BROKEN BOTTLE
LOOKS JUST LIKE A DIAMOND RING
BUT IT'S FAR FAR FROM ME

WELL I LEANED ON MY LEFT LEG
IN THE PARKING LOT DIRT
AND CATHY WAS ~~LOCKING THE DOOR~~   *Closing the lites*
A JUNE BUG FLEW FROM THE ~~DIRT~~ HE ONCE KNEW   *warmth*
~~AND I DREAMED OF US AS BEFORE~~   *and I wished for once I weren't right*
~~WHEN,~~WE USED TO LAUGH TOGETHER
AND DANCE TO ANY OLD SONG
WELL , YOU KNOW SHE STILL LAUGHS WITH ME
BUT SHE WAITS JUST A SECOND TOO LONG

        REPEAT CHORUS

WELL I STARTED THE ENGINE
AND I GAVE IT SOME GAS
AND CATHY WAS CLOSING HER PURSE
WELL WE HADN'T GONE FAR
IN MY BEAT UP OLD CAR
AND I WAS PREPARED FOR THE WORST
WILL YOU STILL SEE ME TOMARROW
NO, I GOT TOO MUCH TO DO
ÞECCÞGÞ A QUESTION AIN'T REALLY A QUESTION
IF YOU KNOW THE ANSWER TOO

        REPEAT CHORUS

FISH AND WHISTLE

Written by John Prine

G   C G
I been thinking lately about the people I meet
 C   G   D
The carwash on the corner and the hole in the street
 G   C
The way my ankles hurt with shoes on my feet
    G   D   G
And I'm wondering if I'm gonna see tomorrow

G   C   G
Father forgive us for what we must do
C   G D
You forgive us, we'll forgive you
G   C
We'll forgive each other 'til we both turn blue
**   G   D   G**
Then we'll whistle and go fishing in Heaven

G   C   G
I was in the army but I never dug a trench
C   G   D
I used to bust my knuckles on a monkey wrench
    G   C
Then I'd go to town and drink and give the girls a pinch
    G   D   G
But I don't think they ever even noticed me

G   C   G
Father forgive us for what we must do
C   G D
You forgive us, we'll forgive you
G   C
We'll forgive each other 'til we both turn blue
**   G   D   G**
Then we'll whistle and go fishing in Heaven

D
Fish and whistle, whistle and fish
G
Eat everything that they put on your dish

C   G
And when we get through we'll make a big wish
*   A   D*
That we never have to do this again, again, again

       G   C   G
On my very first job I said thank you and please
C   G   D
They made me scrub a parking lot down on my knees
G   C
Then I got fired for being scared of bees
    G   D   G
And they only give me fifty cents an hour

G   C   G
Father forgive us for what we must do
C   G D
You forgive us, we'll forgive you
G   C
We'll forgive each other 'til we both turn blue
**   G   D   G**
Then we'll whistle and go fishing in Heaven

D
Fish and whistle, whistle and fish
G
Eat everything that they put on your dish
*   C   G*
And when we get through we'll make a big wish
*   A   D*
That we never have to do this again, again, again

G   C   G
Father forgive us for what we must do
C   G D
You forgive us, we'll forgive you
G   C
We'll forgive each other 'til we both turn blue
**   G   D   G**
Then we'll whistle and go fishing in Heaven

This is my Dad after a day of fishing though he never put a pole in the water! It's a long story ... but ice cold beer, and a good friend called Bubby Short always saved the day.

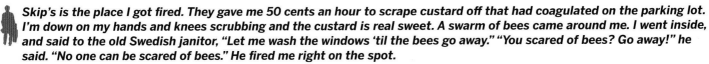 *Skip's is the place I got fired. They gave me 50 cents an hour to scrape custard off that had coagulated on the parking lot. I'm down on my hands and knees scrubbing and the custard is real sweet. A swarm of bees came around me. I went inside, and said to the old Swedish janitor, "Let me wash the windows 'til the bees go away." "You scared of bees? Go away!" he said. "No one can be scared of bees." He fired me right on the spot.*

GLORY OF TRUE LOVE
Written by John Prine and Roger Cook

A   D   A
Oh the glory of true love is a wild and precious thing
               E   A
It don't grow on old magnolias or only blossom in the spring
            D   A
No the glory of true love is it will last your whole life through
          E   A
Never will go out of fashion, always will look good on you

     A   D
You can climb the highest mountain
            A
Touch the moon and stars above
           E
But Old Faithful's just a fountain
             A
Compared to the glory of true love

A   D   A
Long before I met you darling, Lord I thought I had it all
               E   A
I could have my lunch in London and my dinner in St. Paul
                 D   A
I got some friends in Albuquerque where the governor calls me "Gov"
            E   A
You can give 'em all to Goodwill for the glory of true love

     A   D
You can climb the highest mountain
            A
Touch the moon and stars above
            E
But Old Faithful's just a fountain
             A
Compared to the glory of true love

A   D   A
Glory, glory, glory, glory, you can't never get enough
               E   A
Time alone will tell the story of the glory of true love

GRANDPA WAS A CARPENTER
Written by John Prine

Capo on 2nd Fret

G   C
Grandpa wore his suit to dinner nearly every day
                       G   D
No particular reason, he just dressed that way
 G   C
A brown necktie and a matching vest and both his wingtip shoes
                     G   D   G
He built a closet on our back porch and put a penny in a burned out fuse

C   G
Grandpa was a carpenter, he built houses, stores and banks
C   G   D
Chain-smoked Camel cigarettes and hammered nails in planks
**   G   C**
He was level on the level, he shaved even every door
**   G   D   G**
And voted for Eisenhower cause Lincoln won the war

G   C
Well he used to sing me "Blood on the Saddle" and rock me on his knee
                       G   D
And let me listen to the radio before we got TV
        G   C
Well he'd drive to church on Sunday and he'd take me with him too
                   G   D   G
Stained glass in every window, hearing aids in every pew

C   G
Grandpa was a carpenter, he built houses, stores and banks
C   G   D
Chain-smoked Camel cigarettes and hammered nails in planks
**   G   C**
He was level on the level, he shaved even every door
**   G   D   G**
And voted for Eisenhower cause Lincoln won the war

G   C
Now my grandma was a teacher, went to school in Bowling Green
                    G   D
Traded in a milking cow for a Singer sewing machine
        G   C
Well she called her husband "Mister" and she walked real tall and pride
                   G   D   G
And she used to buy me comic books after grandpa died

C   G
Grandpa was a carpenter, he built houses, stores and banks
C   G   D
Chain-smoked Camel cigarettes and hammered nails in planks
**   G   C**
He was level on the level, he shaved even every door
**   G   D   G**
And voted for Eisenhower cause Lincoln won the war

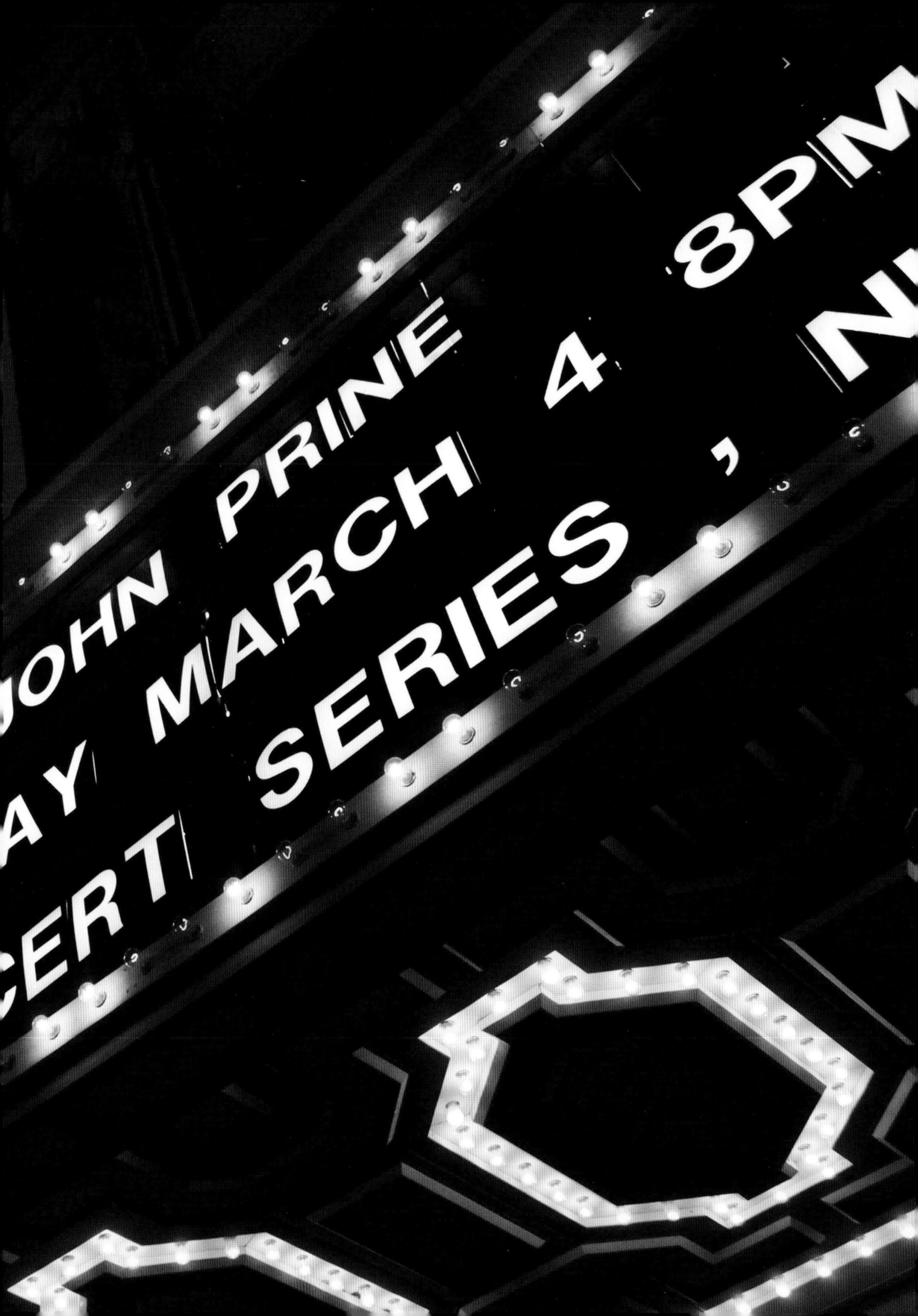
JOHN PRINE
AY MARCH 4 8PM
CERT SERIES ,

HELLO IN THERE

Written by John Prine

Capo on 5th Fret

G   Am   D7
We had an apartment in the city
G   Am   D7
Me and Loretta liked living there
Bm   C
Well it'd been years since the kids had grown
      G   D
A life of their own, left us alone

G   Am   D7
John and Linda live in Omaha
G   Am   D7
And Joe is somewhere on the road
Bm   C
We lost Davy in the Korean War
           G   D
And I still don't know what for, don't matter anymore

F   G
You know that old trees just grow stronger
       F   G
And old rivers grow wilder everyday
Bm   C
Old people just grow lonesome
        G   D   G
Waiting for someone to say, "Hello in there, hello"

G   Am   D7
Me and Loretta, we don't talk much more
G   Am   D7
She sits and stares through the back door screen
Bm   C
And all the news just repeats itself
           G   D
Like some forgotten dream that we've both seen

G   Am   D7
Someday I'll go and call up Rudy
G   Am   D7
We worked together at the factory
Bm   C
But what could I say if he asks, "What's new"
         G   D
"Nothing, what's with you, nothing much to do"

F   G
You know that old trees just grow stronger
       F   G
And old rivers grow wilder everyday
Bm   C
Old people just grow lonesome
        G   D   G
Waiting for someone to say, "Hello in there, hello"

G   Am   D7
So if you're out walking down the street sometime
G   Am   D7
And spot some hollow ancient eyes
Bm   C
Please don't just pass them by and stare
        G   D   G
As if you didn't care, say, "Hello in there, hello"

HOW LUCKY

Written by John Prine

```
        E                                A
Today I walked down a street I used to wander
              E                          B
Yeah I shook my hand and I made myself a bet
                    E                        A
Well there was all these things that I don't think I remember
        E          B        E
Hey how lucky can one man get


   E                                              A
I bronzed my shoes and I hung 'em from my rear view mirror
              E                    B
Bronzed admiration in a blind spot of regret
                    E                      A
There was all these things that I don't think I remember
        E          B        E
Hey how lucky can one man get


        E                           A
Today I walked down a street I used to wander
                 E                  B
Yeah I scratched my head and I lit my cigarette
                        E                        A
Well there was all these things that I don't think I remember
        E          B        E
Hey how lucky can one man get


        E                           A
Today I walked down a street I used to wander
                 E                  B
Yeah I shook my hand and I made myself a bet
                    E                        A
Well there was all these things that I don't think I remember
        E          B        E
Hey how lucky can one man get
```

I JUST WANT TO DANCE WITH YOU

Written by John Prine and Roger Cook

C   G7
I don't want to be the kind to hesitate, be too shy, wait too late

                                                             C
I don't care what they say other lovers do, I just want to dance with you

                                                     G7
I got a feeling that you have a heart like mine, so let it show, let it shine

                                                         C
For if we have a chance to make one heart of two, then I just want to dance with you

              F   **C**
I want to dance with you, twirl you all around the floor
              G7   **C**
That's what they invented dancing for, I just want to dance with you
              F   **C**
I want to dance with you, hold you in my arms once more
              G7   **C**
That's what they invented dancing for, I just want to dance with you

C   G7
I caught you looking at me when I looked at you, yes I did, ain't that true

                                                              C
You won't get embarrassed by the things I do, I just want to dance with you

                                                     G7
Oh the boys are playing softly and the girls are too, so am I, and so are you

                                                     C
If this were a movie we'd be right on cue, I just want to dance with you

              F   **C**
I want to dance with you, twirl you all around the floor
              G7   **C**
That's what they invented dancing for, I just want to dance with you
              F   **C**
I want to dance with you, hold you in my arms once more
              G7   **C**
That's what they invented dancing for, I just want to dance with you

I would have been a good pool player if I had learned to hold a better bridge. Guy who owned the pool hall told me, "It doesn't matter what you see, you can't hit it right unless you're holding your bridge right...you're not going to be hitting what you're aiming for."

IN SPITE OF OURSELVES

Written by John Prine

C
She don't like her eggs all runny

She thinks crossin' her legs is funny
F
She looks down her nose at money
C
She gets it on like the Easter Bunny
G
She's my baby, I'm her honey
                        C
I'm never gonna let her go

C
He ain't got laid in a month of Sundays

I caught him once and he was sniffin' my undies
F
He ain't too sharp but he gets things done
C
Drinks his beer like it's oxygen
G
He's my baby, and I'm his honey
                        C
I'm never gonna let him go

C   F   C
In spite of ourselves, we'll end up sittin' on a rainbow
        G   C
Against all odds, honey we're the big door prize
            F   C
We're gonna spite our noses right off of our faces
            C   G   C
There won't be nothin' but big old hearts dancin' in our eyes

C
She thinks all my jokes are corny

Convict movies make her horny
F
She likes ketchup on her scrambled eggs
C
Swears like a sailor when she shaves her legs
G
She takes a lickin' and keeps on tickin'
                        C
I'm never gonna let her go

C
He's got more balls than a big brass monkey

He's a whacked out weirdo and a lovebug junkie
F
Sly as a fox and crazy as a loon
C
Payday comes and he's howlin' at the moon
G
He's my baby, I don't mean maybe
                        C
I'm never gonna let him go

C   F   C
In spite of ourselves, we'll end up sittin' on a rainbow
        G   C
Against all odds, honey we're the big door prize
            F   C
We're gonna spite our noses right off of our faces
            C   G   C
There won't be nothin' but big old hearts dancin' in our eyes

IT'S A BIG OLD GOOFY WORLD

Written by John Prine

```
G                    C
Up in the morning, work like a dog
 D                      C          G
Is better than sitting like a bump on a log
                              C
Mind all your manners, be quiet as a mouse
            D                     C       G
Someday you'll own a home that's as big as a house
```

```
G                    C
I know a fella, he eats like a horse
D                          C        G
Knocks his old balls 'round the old golf course
                                 C
You oughta see his wife, she's a cute little dish
           D                     C          G
She smokes like a chimney and drinks like a fish
```

```
          G
There's a big old goofy man
           C
Dancing with a big old goofy girl
D                        G
Ooh baby, it's a big old goofy world
```

```
G                          C
Elvis had a woman with a head like a rock
 D                    C            G
I wished I had a woman that made my knees knock
                      C
She'd sing like an angel and eat like a bird
        D                      C      G
And if I wrote a song, she'd know every single word
```

```
          G
There's a big old goofy man
           C
Dancing with a big old goofy girl
D                        G
Ooh baby, it's a big old goofy world
```

```
G                          C
Kiss a little baby, give the world a smile
        D                  C            G
And if you take an inch, give 'em back a mile
                                        C
Cause if you lie like a rug and you don't give a damn
          D                  C       G
You're never gonna be as happy as a clam
```

```
        G                  C
I'm sitting in a hotel trying to write a song
        D                       C    G
My head is just as empty as the day is long
                               C
Why it's clear as a bell, I should've gone to school
            D                 C         G
I'd be wise as an owl, instead of stubborn as a mule
```

```
          G
There's a big old goofy man
           C
Dancing with a big old goofy girl
D                        G
Ooh baby, it's a big old goofy world
```

My working list from Big Old Goofy World. My Mom and I came up with a list originally, off a puzzle page. I called friends from all over, England and everywhere, to get these similes. People started giving me ones from overseas that I didn't know anything about.

Big old Goofy World

Head Like a Rock
Lies like a Rug
Smoke like a Chimney
Drink like a Fish
Cool as a Cucumber
~~Eats~~ Eats like a Bird
~~Sleeps~~ Sings like an Angel
Dumb As The Day is long
Dumb as a Barrel of ~~Hair~~ Hair
Busy as a Bee
Sweats like a Pig
Works like The ~~Dog~~ Devil
Tuff as nails
Scared as a Rabbit
Runs like the wind
~~Treated~~ Treated like a Dog
~~Sits~~ ~~There~~ like a bump on a Log
Eats like a Horse
Smart as a Whip
Slow as molasses
Sweet as Sugar
ITS RAINING CATS & DOGS
Clear as Day, Black as nite
Clear as a Bell
Hotter than The Hubs of Hell
Built like a Brick Shithouse
Cold as a Welldiggers Ass
Sharp as a Tack
Stubborn as a ~~Mule~~ Mule
Strong as an Ox

Happy
as
a
Clam

cute as
a butter

Pleased
as
Punch

Proud
as
a Peacock

741-3954

JESUS;::THE MISSING YEARS

by

~~john prine~~ A MINISERIES BY JOHN E. PRINE

IT WAS RAINING, IT WAS COLD

WEST BETHLEHAM WAS NO PLACE FOR A TWELVE YEAR OLD

SO HE PACKED HIS BAGS AND HE HEADED OUT

TO FIND OUT WHAT THE WORLD,S ABOUT *was*

HE WENT TO FRANCE,HE WENT TO SPAIN *Germany*

HE FOUND LOVE,HE FOUND PAIN *+Happiness*

HE FOUND STORES,SO HE STARTED TO SHOP

BUT HE HAD NO MONEY, SO HE KILLED A COP

~~AT LEAST HE THOUGHT HE DID~~

COP KILLIN KIDS FROM ISRAEL DIDN,T HAVE NO HOME *much of a Hom*

SO HE ~~CUTXED~~ HIS ~~HAGR~~ AND MOVED TO ROME

IT WAS THERE HE MET HIS IRISH BRIDE

AND THEY RENTED A FLAT ON THE LOWER EAST SIDE *MONEY CHAN CARPE BOOKBINDERS B*

OF ROME ITALY THAT IS ,,,,SWIMMING POOLS, MUSIC PUBLISHERS

MUSIC PUBLISHERS & PRETTY LITTLE ITALIAN CHIC

Book Binders Moneychangers Swimming Poo orgies & Lolo

WINE WAS FLOWING,SO WERE BEERS

SO JESUS FOUND HIS MISSING YEARS

HE WENT TO A DANCE AND SAID THIS DON,T MOVE ME

SO HE HIKED UP HIS PANTS AND WENT TO A MOVIE

somewhere around

ON HIS THIRTEENTH BIRTHDAY

HE SAW "REBEL WITHOUT A CAUSE"

HE WENT STRAIGHT ON HOME

AND INVENTED SANTA CLAUS

WHO GAVE HIM A GIFT AND HE RESPONDED IN KIND *Don't mind Chord*

HE GAVE THE GIFT OF LOVE

AND WENT OUT OF HIS MIND

JESUS THE MISSING YEARS

Written by John Prine

(Spoken)
C F G

It was raining, it was cold
West Bethlehem was no place for a twelve year old
So he packed his bags and he headed out
To find out what the world's about
He went to France, he went to Spain
He found love, he found pain
He found stores, so he started to shop
But he had no money, so he got in trouble with a cop
Kids in trouble with the cops from Israel didn't have no home
So he cut his hair and moved to Rome
It was there he met his Irish bride
And they rented a flat on the lower east side of Rome, Italy that is
Music publishers, book binders, Bible belters
Swimming pools, orgies and lots of pretty Italian chicks

C   F
Charley bought some popcorn, Billy bought a car
G   C
Someone almost bought the farm, but they didn't go that far
                        F
Things shut down at midnight, at least around here they do
            G   C
Cause we all reside down the block inside at 23 Skidoo

(Spoken)
C F G

Wine was flowing, so were beers
So Jesus found his missing years
He went to a dance and said, "This don't move me"
He hiked up his pants and he went to a movie
On his thirteenth birthday, he saw "Rebel Without A Cause"
He went straight on home and invented Santa Claus
Who gave him a gift, and he responded in kind
He gave the gift of love and went out of his mind
You see him and the wife wasn't getting along
So he took out his guitar and he wrote a song
Called "The Dove Of Love Fell Off The Perch"
But he couldn't get divorced in the Catholic Church
At least not back then anyhow
Jesus was a good guy, he didn't need this shit
So he took a pill with a Coca-Cola, and he swallowed it
He discovered the Beatles, and he recorded with the Stones
Once he even opened up a three-way package for old George Jones

C   F
Charley bought some popcorn, Billy bought a car
G   C
Someone almost bought the farm, but they didn't go that far
                        F
Things shut down at midnight, at least around here they do
            G   C
Cause we all reside down the block inside at 23 Skidoo

(Spoken)
C F G

The years went by like sweet little days
With babies crying pork chops and Beaujolais
When he woke up, he was seventeen
The world was angry, the world was mean
Why the man down the street and the kid on the stoop
All agreed that life stank, all the world smelled like poop
Baby poop that is, the worst kind
So he grew his hair long and threw away his comb
And headed back to Jerusalem to find Mom and Dad and home
But when he got there the cupboard was bare
Except for an old black man with a fishing rod
He said, "Whatcha gonna be when you grow up"
Jesus said, "God"
Oh my God, what have I gotten myself into
I'm a human corkscrew and all my wine is blood
They're gonna kill me Mama, they don't like me Bud
So Jesus went to Heaven, and he went there awful quick
All them people killed him, and he wasn't even sick
So come and gather around me, my contemporary peers
And I'll tell you all the story of "Jesus The Missing Years"

C   F
Charley bought some popcorn, Billy bought a car
G   C
Someone almost bought the farm, but they didn't go that far
                        F
Things shut down at midnight, at least around here they do
            G   C
Cause we all reside down the block inside at 23 Skidoo

 I recorded this onto a cassette at about four in the morning. The next day I typed it off of the cassette and then made changes as I was going through. I like to write with a typewriter because I type slow - it gives me time to edit.

LAKE MARIE

Written by John Prine

```
D     G     C
We were standing
D               G     C
Standing by peaceful waters
D               G
Standing by peaceful waters
C         D     G
Whoa Wah Oh Wah Oh
```

(Spoken)
```
G    C   D
```
Many years ago, along the Illinois-Wisconsin border
There was this Indian tribe
They found two babies in the woods, white babies
One of them was named Elizabeth
She was the fairer of the two
While the smaller and more fragile one was named Marie
Having never seen white girls before
And living on the two lakes known as the Twin Lakes
They named the larger and more beautiful lake, Lake Elizabeth
And thus the smaller lake that was hidden from the highway
Became known forever as Lake Marie

```
D     G     C
We were standing
D               G     C
Standing by peaceful waters
D               G
Standing by peaceful waters
C         D     G
Whoa Wah Oh Wah Oh
```

(Spoken)
```
G    C   D
```
Many years later I found myself talking to this girl
Who was standing there with her back turned to Lake Marie
The wind was blowing, especially through her hair
There was four Italian sausages cooking on the outdoor grill
And they was sizzlin'
Many years later, we found ourselves in Canada
Trying to save our marriage and perhaps catch a few fish
Whatever came first
That night she fell asleep in my arms, humming the tune to
"Louie Louie"
Aah baby, we gotta go now

```
D     G     C
We were standing
D               G     C
Standing by peaceful waters
D               G
Standing by peaceful waters
C         D     G
Whoa Wah Oh Wah Oh
```

(Spoken)
```
G    C   D
```
The dogs were barking as the cars were parking
The loan sharks were sharking, the narcs were narcing
Practically everyone was there
In the parking lot by the forest preserve
The police had found two bodies, nay, naked bodies
Their faces had been horribly disfigured by some sharp object
Saw it on the news, the TV news, in a black and white video
You know what blood looks like in a black and white video
Shadows, shadows, that's what it looks like
All the love we shared between her and me was slammed
Slammed up against the banks of Old Lake Marie, Marie

```
D     G     C
We were standing
D               G     C
Standing by peaceful waters
D               G
Standing by peaceful waters
C         D     G
Whoa Wah Oh Wah Oh
```

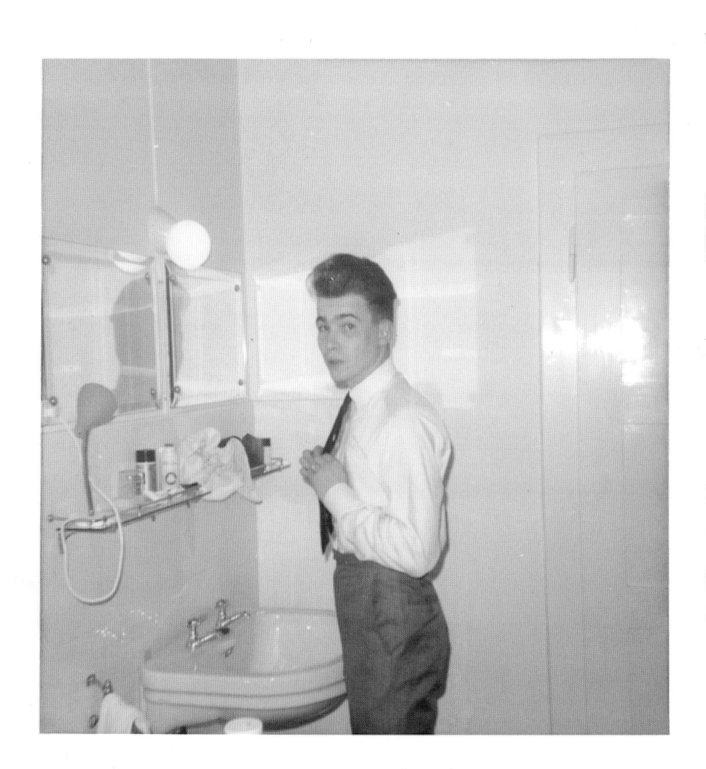

LET'S TALK DIRTY IN HAWAIIAN
Written by John Prine and Fred Koller

       C   G
Well I packed my bags and bought myself a ticket for the land of the tall palm tree

                               C
Aloha Old Milwaukee, hello Waikiki

                                            F
I just stepped down from the airplane, when I heard her say

                      C   G   C
"Wacka wacka nooka licka, wacka wacka nooka licka, would you like a lei," hey

C   G
Let's talk dirty in Hawaiian, whisper in my ear

                                            C
Kicka pooka mok a wa wahine are the words I long to hear

                                               F
Lay your coconutta on my tiki, what the hecka mooka mooka dear

                  C   A7   F   G   C
Let's talk dirty in Hawaiian, say the words I long to hear

       C   G
It's a ukulele Honolulu sunset, listen to the grass skirts sway

                                        C
Drinking rum from a pineapple out on Honolulu Bay

                                          F
The steel guitars are playing, while she's talking with her hands

                                C   G   C
"Gimme gimme oka-doka, make a wisha wanna polka," words I understand, hey

C   G
Let's talk dirty in Hawaiian, whisper in my ear

                                            C
Kicka pooka mok a wa wahine are the words I long to hear

                                               F
Lay your coconutta on my tiki, what the hecka mooka mooka dear

                  C   A7   F   G   C
Let's talk dirty in Hawaiian, say the words I long to hear

       C   G
Well I boughta lotta junka with my moola and sent it to the folks back home

                                           C
I never had a chance to dance the hula, well I guess I should have known

                                           F
When you start talking to the sweet wahine, walking in the pale moonlight

                                C   G   C
"Ohka noka whatta setta, knocka-rocka-sis-boom-boccas," hope I said it right, oh

C   G
Let's talk dirty in Hawaiian, whisper in my ear

                                            C
Kicka pooka mok a wa wahine are the words I long to hear

                                               F
Lay your coconutta on my tiki, what the hecka mooka mooka dear

                  C   A7   F   G   C
Let's talk dirty in Hawaiian, say the words I long to hear

 Me and Fred Kohler wrote this on the patio of the Rock n Roll Hotel in Nashville, back in the 80's. Fred had the idea for the title and I thought, "Oh yeah, I like that." I had this little book I'd bought in Waikiki years earlier. One of those goofy little books about how to speak Hawaiian. I thought it would give us some ideas for words. Instead we threw the book away and made up all our Hawaiian words. So they all sounded dirty. 'Cause the song is basically: "Come-on-I-wanna-lay-ya"

LINDA GOES TO MARS

Written by John Prine

D   G
I just found out yesterday that Linda goes to Mars
A   D
Every time I sit and look at pictures of used cars
                          G
She'll turn on her radio and sit down in her chair
    A   D
And look at me across the room, as if I wasn't there

D G D   G
Oh my stars, my Linda's gone to Mars
**   A   D**
Well I wish she wouldn't leave me here alone
D G D   G
Oh my stars, my Linda's gone to Mars
**   A   D**
Well I wonder will she bring me something home

D   G
Something, somewhere, somehow took my Linda by the hand
    A   D
And secretly decoded our sacred wedding band
                            G
For when the moon shines down upon our happy, humble home
    A   D
Her inner space gets tortured by some outer space unknown

D G D   G
Oh my stars, my Linda's gone to Mars
**   A   D**
Well I wish she wouldn't leave me here alone
D G D   G
Oh my stars, my Linda's gone to Mars
**   A   D**
Well I wonder will she bring me something home

D   G
Now I ain't seen no saucers 'cept the ones upon the shelf
    A   D
And if I ever seen one I'd keep it to myself
                            G
For if there's life out there somewhere beyond this life on earth
    A   D
Then Linda must have gone out there and got her money's worth

D G D   G
Oh my stars, my Linda's gone to Mars
**   A   D**
Well I wish she wouldn't leave me here alone
D G D   G
Oh my stars, my Linda's gone to Mars
**   A   D**
Well I wonder will she bring me something home

1984½ Jan 2, 1975

Jehosofat the mongrel cat
Jumped off the roof today
Some say he Fell
But I could Tell
He did himself away
His ~~the~~ Eyes weren't Bright
Like they were the night
We played checkers on The Train
Goddamn His Soul
He was a Tootsie Roll
But he's a dead cat just the same

Chorus
We are living in the Future
I'll tell you how I know
I read it in the Paper
Fifteen Years ago
We're all driving Rocket Ships
and Talking with our minds
and wearing Turquise Jewelery
and standing in Soup Lines

LIVING IN THE FUTURE

Written by John Prine

```
E                                           A
Jehosaphat the mongrel cat jumped off the roof today
                    E         B7      E
Some say he fell but I could tell he did himself away

His eyes weren't bright like they were the night
                          A
We played checkers on the train
                              E
God bless his soul, he was a tootsie roll
        B7              E
But he's a dead cat just the same

        A         E       A          E
We are living in the future, I'll tell you how I know
   A        E    B7       E
I read it in the paper fifteen years ago
A          E              A              E
We're all driving rocket ships and talking with our minds
       A            E        B7           E
And wearing turquoise jewelry and standing in soup lines
        B7            E
We're standing in soup lines

E                                                     A
Jake the barber's lonely daughter went down to her Daddy's shop
                        E                 B7        E
She plugged herself to a barber pole and took a little off the top

There was pressure on the left, pressure on the right
                          A
Pressure in the middle of the hole
                            E
I'm going to Maine on a forty foot crane
        B7              E
I'm gonna use it for a fishing pole

        A         E       A          E
We are living in the future, I'll tell you how I know
   A        E    B7       E
I read it in the paper fifteen years ago
A          E              A              E
We're all driving rocket ships and talking with our minds
       A            E        B7           E
And wearing turquoise jewelry and standing in soup lines
        B7            E
We're standing in soup lines
```

```
E                                              A
Old Sarah Brown sells tickets down at the all night picture show
                              E
Where they grind out sex and they rate it with an "X"
        B7                    E
Just to make a young man's pants grow

No tops, no bottoms, just hands and feet

Screaming the posters out on the street

Strangling the curious and the weak
        B7                    E
Hell we give 'em what they want to see-o
        B7                    E
Hell we give 'em what they want to see-o

        A         E       A          E
We are living in the future, I'll tell you how I know
   A        E    B7       E
I read it in the paper fifteen years ago
A          E              A              E
We're all driving rocket ships and talking with our minds
       A            E        B7           E
And wearing turquoise jewelry and standing in soup lines
        B7            E
We're standing in soup lines
```

 I started writing this song in 1975 and I didn't finish it until '86. It was all because of the last verse. So I finally x'ed that verse out and wrote a different one.

LONG MONDAY

Written by John Prine and Keith Sykes

Capo on 3rd Fret

```
G              C                    G
You and me, sittin' in the back of my memory
                   C                   G
Like a honey bee, buzzin' 'round a glass of sweet Chablis
D        C                      G
Radio's on, windows rolled up, and my mind's rolled down
D                    C               G
Headlights shinin' like silver moons rollin' on the ground

G              C            G
We made love in every way love can be made
                   C                G
And we made time feel like time could never fade
D          C              G
Friday night we both made the guitar hum
D              C                 D
Saturday made Sunday feel like it would never come

           G
Gonna be a long Monday
C                                        G
Sittin' all alone on a mountain by a river that has no end

Gonna be a long Monday
D                                    C    G
Stuck like the tick of a clock that's come unwound, again

G              C            G
Soul to soul, heart to heart and cheek to cheek
                   C                G
Come on baby, give me a kiss that'll last all week
        D           C        G
The thought of you leavin' again brings me down
        D        C              D
The promise of your sweet love brings me around

           G
Gonna be a long Monday
C                                        G
Sittin' all alone on a mountain by a river that has no end

Gonna be a long Monday
D                                    C
Stuck like the tick of a clock that's come unwound
D          G
Again and again
```

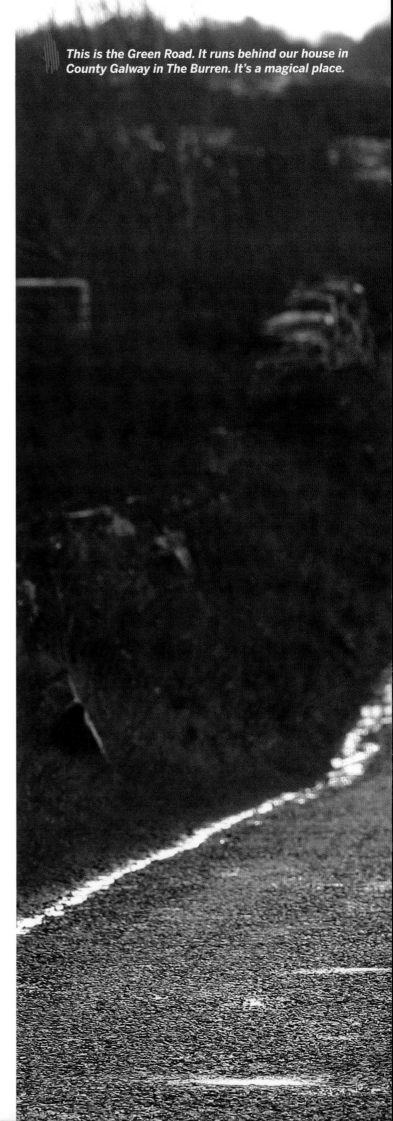

This is the Green Road. It runs behind our house in County Galway in The Burren. It's a magical place.

LOVE, LOVE, LOVE

Written by John Prine and Keith Sykes

```
E                       A          B7
He stumbled through the alley with his long coat on
A          B7          E
Nothing but a bottle in his hand
                A                    B7
She sat in her apartment lonesome to the bone
A                    B7              E
Wondering what had happened to her man
```

```
E    A    E    B7   A    B7        E
Love, love, love, love, nobody ever understands
         A     E   B7  A     B7          E
All the things that go between a woman and a man
```

```
E                       A          B7
When they'd walk down the sidewalk the street would shine
         A          B7              E
With the kind of love no human heart can fake
                        A          B7
And they vowed to stay together 'til the end of time
         A                    B7          E
Like the couple that stands on top of the wedding cake
```

```
E    A    E    B7   A    B7        E
Love, love, love, love, nobody ever understands
         A     E   B7  A     B7          E
All the things that go between a woman and a man
```

```
E          A     B7
If I should live to a ripe old age
       A          B7        E
The only lesson I may ever learn
                A          B7
Is to not stand so close to the flame of love
     A          B7        E
Unless you are willing to get burned
```

```
E    A    E    B7   A    B7        E
Love, love, love, love, nobody ever understands
         A     E   B7  A     B7          E
All the things that go between a woman and a man
```

MAUREEN, MAUREEN

Written by John Prine

G   C   G/B   Am
Maureen, Maureen, I shot a doctor last night on the airplane
            D   G
Well they said he wouldn't hurt us, but he got me real nervous and mean
                                                                                C   G/B   Am
He was fat and he stank, and God knows that he drank more than we do
        D   G
So I shot him in the first class, then I bailed out and ran home to you

G   C   G
But you don't believe me, I could tell by your smile
                        C   D   D7
Honey, why don't you leave me, get lost for awhile, Maureen

G   C   G/B   Am
Maureen, Maureen, there's a hole in between where we come from
            D   G
And the things that I'm thinking, ain't necessarily the things that I say
                                                                    C   G/B   Am
I may have lied to myself, but I tried to tell God how I love you
            D   G
But even He don't answer His phone anymore when I pray

G   C   G
But you don't believe me, I could tell by your smile
                        C   D   D7
Honey, why don't you leave me, get lost for awhile, Maureen

G   C   G/B   Am
Maureen, Maureen, I shot a doctor last night on the airplane
            D   G
Well they said he wouldn't hurt us, but he got me real nervous and mean

Oh You

Yesterday Morning a tornado come
and blew your picture right
   outta the frame
It even blew the candle out
From under The flame
That burned beneath the love
We once knew
Whatever happened to you?

Some people are rich
Some people are poor
Some are rotten
right to the core
The licquor that the boilermaker blew
That horse runs slower than glue
Tested arrested

Maureen Maureen there's a hole
in between where we come from
The things that I'm thinkin
ain't necessarilly the things that I say
If I could unwind
this knot in my mind
and just speak my mind
Truth can be cruel

I'll wink!

Believe me
cruel

hot fools
glow
FOLLOW HER
HOME
To see what her
mother looks like

MEXICAN HOME

Written by John Prine

C F C   F
It got so hot last night, I swear you couldn't hardly breathe
 C   G7 C F G7
Heat lightning burnt the sky like alcohol
C   F   C   F
I sat on the porch without my shoes and I watched the cars roll by
 C   G7   C F C
As the headlights raced to the corner of the kitchen wall

F   C   F   C
Mama dear, your boy is here, far across the sea
F   C   G7
Waiting for that sacred core that burns inside of me
  C   F   C   F
And I feel a storm all wet and warm, not ten miles away
  C G7 C
Approaching my Mexican home

C   F   C   F
"My God," I cried, it's so hot inside you could die in the living room
  C   G7   C F G7
Take the fan from the window, prop the door back with a broom
  C   F   C   F
The cuckoo clock has died of shock and the windows feel no pane
  C G7   C F C
The air's as still as the throttle on a funeral train

F   C   F   C
Mama dear, your boy is here, far across the sea
F   C   G7
Waiting for that sacred core that burns inside of me
  C   F   C   F
And I feel a storm all wet and warm, not ten miles away
  C G7 C
Approaching my Mexican home

   C   F   C   F
My father died on the porch outside on an August afternoon
     C   G7   C F G7
I sipped bourbon and cried with a friend by the light of the moon
    C   F   C   F
So its hurry, hurry, step right up, it's a matter of life or death
    C   G7   C F C
The sun is going down and the moon is just holding its breath

F   C   F   C
Mama dear, your boy is here, far across the sea
F   C   G7
Waiting for that sacred core that burns inside of me
   C   F   C   F
And I feel a storm all wet and warm, not ten miles away
  C G7 C
Approaching my Mexican home

ONE RED ROSE

Written by John Prine

```
G                       D
The rain came down on the tin roof hardly
   C                     D
A sound was left from the birthday party
C              D              G   D
The kitchen light fell asleep on the bedroom floor
G                    D
Well me and her were talking softer
C                  D
Than all the time before I lost her
C        D              G
Picture sat on top of the chest of drawers
```

```
C      D      G
One red rose in the Bible
C              G        D
Pressed between the holy alphabet
C                D               G
Probably wouldn't believe you if you told me
            C         D         G
But what I never knew I never will forget
```

```
G          D
Rainy nights get dark real early
C                       D
Her dress was soft and her hair was curly
C                D            G D
We danced around the table to the old banjo
G              D
Rainy nights were made for lovers
C               D
We lay there still beneath the covers
C       D              G
And I ain't never felt like that before
```

```
C      D      G
One red rose in the Bible
C              G        D
Pressed between the holy alphabet
C                D               G
Probably wouldn't believe you if you told me
            C         D         G
But what I never knew I never will forget
```

Me and Goodman always believed in fine food, fine wine, fine friends, and fine women. We had some really great meals. I love that shirt. I don't know where it is today but I got a lot of use out of it back then.

After my Dad died, my Mom wanted to get out of the house right away. We moved her into an apartment. This is the first Christmas we spent in that apartment instead of the house we grew up in. It was kind of glum. My first album had come out in October and I was twisted around the world.

ONLY LOVE

Written by John Prine, Roger Cook and Sandy Mason

```
C                              F          C
You may live alone and close your eyes, some folks do
C                              F          C
You may dream a dream that's twice your size all night through
G                        F          C
When the morning comes who's to tell your dreams to
Bb F C
Only you
```

```
C                        F    C
Only love, love only, only love will do
C                        F    C
Only love, love only, only love comes true
G                            F
Nothing else you see, there's nothing else
      C    Bb F C
Only love, only love
```

```
C                        F          C
I have known a love within my heart, one or two
C                              F          C
Where one love would end and one would start I never knew
G                        F          C
If love should come your way you'll learn to say I love you
Bb F    C
I    love you
```

```
C                        F        C
Only love, love only, only love will do
C                        F        C
Only love, love only, only love comes true
G                            F
Nothing else you see, there's nothing else
      C    Bb F C
Only love, only love
```

This is the Paradise General Store and Post Office. If you said, "I need a pack of Kools, a can of beans, and a two cent stamp – he'd sell you the beans and the cigarettes, then he'd put a hat on, a special post master hat, and go inside a cage, like a confession box. He'd have to sell you the stamps through there, you know, because it was official.

POST OF
PARADIS

More Bounce
to the Ounce

Smells Grand...
Packs Right

Smoke
Can

"...The world's largest shovel..." They brought it in piece by piece on a barge down the Green River. Years later when they ran out of coal, they couldn't get the shovel out. It was too expensive to take it out so they buried it. I heard about 100 people gathered and they sang my song while they were burying the shovel. That shovel dug it's own grave.

PEOPLE PUTTIN' PEOPLE DOWN

Written by John Prine

Capo on 2nd Fret

```
A                                    D
People who are sad, sometimes they wear a frown
   A                                 D
And people that are kings, sometimes they wear a crown
        A                            E
But all the people that don't fit get the only fun they get
                     A         D         A
From people puttin' people down, people puttin' people down

A                                    D
People without love sometimes build a fence around
   A                                 D
The garden up above that makes the whole world go 'round
        A                            E
But all the people who don't fit get the only fun they get
                     A         D         A
From people puttin' people down, people puttin' people down

D  A      E      D   E  A
So cold, sometimes it gets so cold

A                                    D
You may lose your wife, you may lose your family
A                                    D
You may lose you mind just to keep your sanity
        A                            E
But the people who don't fit get the only fun they get
                     A         D         A
From people puttin' people down, people puttin' people down

A                                    D
People that are glad, sometimes they wear a smile
   A                                 D
And people without dreams, they walk the extra mile
        A                            E
But all the people who don't fit get the only fun they get
                     A         D         A         D
From people puttin' people down, people puttin' people down
               A         D         A
People puttin' people down, people puttin' people down

D  A      E      D   E  A
So cold, sometimes it gets so cold
```

PICTURE SHOW

Written by John Prine

```
G                                    C              G
A young man from a small town with a very large imagination
   C                 G                           D
Lay alone in his room with his radio on looking for another station
         G                               C            G
When the static from the mouthpiece gave way to the sound below
      C          G                    D                      G
James Dean went out to Hollywood and put his picture in a picture show
```

And it's oh Daddy get off of your knees, Mamma why'd you have to go
```
      G                              C                    G
```
Your darling Jim is out a on limb, I put my picture in a picture show
```
   C          G                   D                   G
```
My picture in a picture show
```
   D                   G
```

```
G                            C              G
Hamburgers, cheeseburgers, Wilbur and Orville Wright
C              G                              D
John Garfield in the afternoon, Montgomery Clift at night
G                                    C              G
When the static hit the mouthpiece, it gave way to the sound below
      C          G                    D                      G
James Dean went out to Hollywood and put his picture in a picture show
```

And it's oh Daddy get off of your knees, Mamma why'd you have to go
```
      G                              C                    G
```
Your darling Jim is out a on limb, I put my picture in a picture show
```
   C          G                   D                   G
```
My picture in a picture show
```
   D                   G
```

```
  G                     C              G
A Mocha man in a wigwam sitting on a reservation
      C                   G                                D
With a big black hole in the belly of his soul waiting on an explanation
          G                                C                 G
While the white man sits on his fat can and takes pictures of the Navajo
      C          G         D              G
Every time he clicks his Kodak pics, he steals a little bit of soul
```

And it's oh Daddy get off of your knees, Mamma why'd you have to go
```
G                                    C                    G
```
Your darling Jim is out a on limb, I put my picture in a picture show
```
   C          G                   D                   G
```
My picture in a picture show
```
   D                   G
```

 I didn't like calling him a brown man. It was Dan Einstein who came up with calling him a Mocha Man. Thanks Dan!

Theres a Brown man
in a Wigwam
That deserves a very
Large Explanation
On why the White man
sits on his Fat can

Theres a Brown Man
in a Wigwam
Sitting on a Reservation
With his whole Soul
With a large Hole
Where his whole Soul
in his lost Soul
Looking For an Explanation

Last nite I had a Terrible dream

~~I was riding down the road in a~~
~~I got~~ ~~with the~~ washin
machine

a John Deer tractor rolled over
my head.
and the very last words that
I said

Please don't bury me down in
the cold cold groun
I'd rather have em cut me up
and pass me all arou
~~throw~~
~~stick~~ my brain in a hurricane
and the blind can have my eyes
and the deaf can take both my ea
if they don't mind th
siz

2ND

Give my stomach to Milwaukee
should they run short of Beer
Put my socks in a cedar box
Just get em out of here
Venus DeMilo can have my arms
look out! I got your nose
Sell my heart to the junkman

Don't pull that stuff on me!
Hand me down my walking cane
It's a sin to tell a lie
Send my mouth Way down South
and kiss my ass, goodbye!

PLEASE DON'T BURY ME

Written by John Prine

D   G
Woke up this morning, put on my slippers
D   A7
Walked in the kitchen and died
 D   G
And oh what a feeling when my soul went through the ceiling
 A7   D
And on up into heaven I did ride

  G   D
When I got there they did say, "John, it happened this way
           A7
You slipped upon the floor and hit your head
 D   G   D
And all the angels say just before you passed away
    A7   D
These were the very last words that you said"

G   D
Please don't bury me down in that cold, cold ground
             A7
No I'd rather have 'em cut me up and pass me all around
D   G   D
Throw my brain in a hurricane and the blind can have my eyes
  G   D   A7   D
And the deaf can take both of my ears if they don't mind the size

D   G   D
Give my stomach to Milwaukee if they run out of beer
      E7   A7
Put my socks in a cedar box just get 'em out of here

D   G   D
Venus de Milo can have my arms, look out I've got your nose
G   D   A7   D
Sell my heart to the junkman and give my love to Rose

G   D
Please don't bury me down in that cold, cold ground
             A7
No I'd rather have 'em cut me up and pass me all around
D   G   D
Throw my brain in a hurricane and the blind can have my eyes
  G   D   A7   D
And the deaf can take both of my ears if they don't mind the size

D   G   D
Give my feet to the footloose, careless, fancy-free
         E7   A7
Give my knees to the needy don't pull that stuff on me
D   G   D
Hand me down my walking cane it's a sin to tell a lie
G   D   A7   D
Send my mouth way down south and kiss my ass goodbye

G   D
Please don't bury me down in that cold, cold ground
             A7
No I'd rather have 'em cut me up and pass me all around
D   G   D
Throw my brain in a hurricane and the blind can have my eyes
  G   D   A7   D
And the deaf can take both of my ears if they don't mind the size

I was playing Central Park. I had Rick playing rhythm guitar and I hired a steel drum player that was on the street to play with me. We played at that big band shell. Same place where Simon and Garfunkel played. Summer of '77.

SAM STONE

Written by John Prine

Capo on 5th Fret

```
C                               F
Sam Stone came home to his wife and family
  G                             C
After serving in the conflict overseas
                                    F
And the time that he served had shattered all his nerves
  G                     C   F  C
And left a little shrapnel in his knee
        F
But the morphine eased the pain

And the grass grew 'round his brain
      D                          G   G7
And gave him all the confidence he lacked
      D                          G   G7
With a Purple Heart and a monkey on his back
```

C   Dm
There's a hole in daddy's arm where all the money goes
F   G
Jesus Christ died for nothing I suppose
**   C   Am**
Little pitchers have big ears, don't stop to count the years
D   G
Sweet songs never last too long on broken radios
**   C   F G**
Mmmhmhmhmm

```
C                               F
Sam Stone's welcome home didn't last too long
G                                 C
He went to work when he'd spent his last dime
                                    F
And Sammy took to stealing when he got that empty feeling
    G                   F    G  C  F  C
For a hundred dollar habit without overtime
        F
And the gold rolled through his veins

Like a thousand railroad trains
      D                          G   G7
And eased his mind in the hours that he chose
          D                          G   G7
While the kids ran around wearing other people's clothes
```

C   Dm
There's a hole in daddy's arm where all the money goes
F   G
Jesus Christ died for nothing I suppose
**   C   Am**
Little pitchers have big ears, don't stop to count the years
D   G
Sweet songs never last too long on broken radios
**   C   F G**
Mmmhmhmhmm

```
C                               F
Sam Stone was alone when he popped his last balloon
G                                 C
Climbing walls while sitting in a chair
                                            F
Well he played his last request while the room smelled just like death
        G       F       G   C  F  C
With an overdose hovering in the air
        F
But life had lost its fun

And there was nothing to be done
      D                              G   G7
But trade his house that he bought on the G.I. Bill
D                              G   G7
For a flag-draped casket on a local heroes' hill
```

C   Dm
There's a hole in daddy's arm where all the money goes
F   G
Jesus Christ died for nothing I suppose
**   C   Am**
Little pitchers have big ears, don't stop to count the years
D   G
Sweet songs never last too long on broken radios
**   C   F G**
Mmmhmhmhmm

At my buddy Mickey's house after boot camp. We got drafted on the same day so we thought we'd end up in the same place. He went to Fort Hood, Texas and I went to Fort Polk, Louisiana. We both came home after boot camp - he went to Vietnam and I went to Germany.

SHE IS MY EVERYTHING

Written by John Prine

```
G   D   G
She is my everything
              C
From her suntanned shoulders
                        G
Down to the freckles on her wedding ring
      C
Her feet are so warm
                           G
They could melt the snow in the early spring
      D   G
She is my everything

G   D   G
She goes everywhere
        C
From Copenhagen to making eggs and bacon
          G
Down in Jackson Square
    C                              G
I'd like to drive a Cadillac the color of her long, black hair
      D   G
She goes everywhere
```

B7   C
Kisses that come all the way from China
*   G   D*
Kinda remind her of memories of Spain
B7   C
If I get lost you can always find her
*   A   D*
Standing right beside me in the rain

```
G   D   G
She uses Eveready
C                                              G
Batteries to keep her electrical appliances going steady
C                                        G
She can do fourteen things at once and then the phone'll ring
      D   G
She is my everything

G   D   G
She knows everybody
          C                                        G
From Muhammad Ali to teaching Bruce Lee how to do karate
              C                                      G
She can lead a parade while putting on her shades in her Maserati
      D   G
She knows everybody
```

B7   C
Kisses that come all the way from China
*   G   D*
Kinda remind her of memories of Spain
B7   C
If I get lost you can always find her
*   A   D*
Standing right beside me in the rain

```
G   D   G
She is my everything
                  C                                          G
When she wakes up in the morning that's when all the birdies start to sing
                  C                        G
When I hear her voice, I'll tell you boys, I forget everything
          D   G
She is my everything
```

6 O'clock News

Wanda had a baby in 1951
an 8 pound bastard strangers son
She called him James Lewis
and gave him a home
  Changed his diapers and Polished his chrome

~~James Lewis grew as fast as he could~~
James grew up and Wanda grew old
The days were long and the nites were co
Jimmy told ~~more~~ lies
Than a lumberjack
Trying to get his mother back

That boy left home on a day in June
and Robbed a bank That afternoon
  Wanda saw Jimmy
in the six o'clock news
With his brains on the sidewalk & blood in the

SIX O'CLOCK NEWS

Written by John Prine

```
G            Em      C          G
Wanda had a baby in Nineteen Fifty-One
             Em          C              D
The father was a stranger and a stranger was the son
C            D       C            D
Call that child James Lewis, call these rooms a home
G            C       D         G
Changing all them diapers, polish all that chrome
C            D            G
C'mon baby, spend the night with me
```

```
G            Em      C          G
All around the schoolyard playing all the games
             Em          C              D
Running, laughing back and forth, the kid with two first names
C            D       C            D
Stranger in the closet, lock the diary
G            C       D         G
The past is running faster, singing harmony
C            D            G
C'mon baby, spend the night with me
```

```
G            Em      C          G
"God bless this kitchen," said the knick-knack shelf
             Em   C          D
"The dinner's almost ready, go and wash yourself"
C            D       C            D
Jimmy's growing up now and Wanda's growing old
G            C       D                 G
The time is growing shorter, the nights are long and cold
C            D            G
C'mon baby, spend the night with me
```

```
G            Em      C          G
Sneaking in the closet and through the diary
             Em      C          D
Now don't you know all he saw was all there was to see
C            D         C    D
The whole town saw Jimmy on the six o'clock news
G            C         D         G
His brains were on the sidewalk and blood was on his shoes
C            D            G
C'mon baby, spend the night with me
```

These are the original lyrics that turned into 6 o'clock News.
I was writing about a kid I knew in my childhood.

SLEEPY EYED BOY

Written by John Prine

D
Where are the bootstraps to lift myself up
G   D
Where is the well where I once filled my cup
G   D
Where does this sorrow all turn into joy
                        A   D
And where oh where is the sleepy eyed boy

D
Where is my true love when the wind starts to moan
     G   D
Is she out in the wildwood, is she there all alone
     G   D
Have I cast her aside like an unwanted toy
                        A   D
Tell me where oh where is the sleepy eyed boy

D
He's going down the backroads in a cold pouring rain
     G   D
He's waiting for a postcard from the south coast of Spain
G   D
Postmarked from a sweetheart back in old Illinois
                        A   D
Saying where oh where is my sleepy eyed boy

D
Where are the bootstraps to lift myself up
G   D
Where is the well where I once filled my cup
G   D
Where does this sorrow all turn into joy
                        A   D
And where oh where is the sleepy eyed boy

SOMEWHERE SOMEONE'S FALLING IN LOVE
Written by John Prine and Donnie Fritts

Capo on 5th Fret

```
C                              F
Well I got time on my hands and I got you on my mind
         C                    F
And the moon and the stars up above
           C            E          Am          D
There's a warm summer breeze blowing down through the trees
        C                 G      C
And somewhere someone's falling in love

C                              F
If this world where we live is the only one we have
            C                        F
Then there's only one thing I'm thinking of
        C         E          Am        D
Let's go for that ride, keep our eyes open wide
          C                 G        C
Cause somewhere someone's falling in love
```

```
F                          C
You may be looking for someone
F                          C
Someone may be looking for you
F                      C
Someday you'll awaken and open your eyes
       D                G
And love will be looking at you
```

```
           C                        F
So don't get down on yourself, no and don't lose your faith
C                                F
Believe these words that I'm singing of
          C         E   Am         D
For just as sure as the day that you were born
C                 G        C
Somewhere someone's falling in love
```

```
F                          C
You may be looking for someone
F                          C
Someone may be looking for you
F                      C
Someday you'll awaken and open your eyes
       D                G
And love will be looking at you
```

```
           C                        F
So don't get down on yourself, no and don't lose your faith
C                                F
Believe these words that I'm singing of
          C         E   Am         D
For just as sure as the day that you were born
C                 G        C
Somewhere someone's falling in love
```

Top: This is from the shoot for 'Somebody Else's Troubles'. It was at Goodman's apartment by Wrigley Field, behind the bleachers on Waveland Avenue. Bottom: The jukebox Goodman gave me because I co-wrote "You Never Even Called Me By My Name". I wouldn't put my name on it cause I thought it sucked. And then it went to number one! That's how I found out what a number one song is...

SOUVENIRS

Written by John Prine

Capo on 5th Fret

```
D                           G    A                           D
All the snow has turned to water, Christmas days have come and gone
                          G      A              D
Broken toys and faded colors are all that's left to linger on
                          G         A              D
I hate graveyards and old pawnshops for they always bring me tears
                          G        A              D
I can't forgive the way they robbed me of my childhood souvenirs
```

A   D
Memories they can't be boughten
A   D
They can't be won at carnivals for free
A   D
Well it took me years to get those souvenirs
**   G   A**
And I don't know how they slipped away from me

```
D                G    A          D
Broken hearts and dirty windows make life difficult to see
                          G      A              D
That's why last night and this morning always look the same to me
                     G     A              D
I hate reading old love letters for they always bring me tears
                          G        A              D
I can't forgive the way they robbed me of my sweetheart's souvenirs
```

A   D
Memories they can't be boughten
A   D
They can't be won at carnivals for free
A   D
Well it took me years to get those souvenirs
**   G   A**
And I don't know how they slipped away from me

SPACE MONKEY

Written by John Prine and Peter Case

G   C   G
Space Monkey, Space Monkey, what you doing up there
                                       D   G
Why it's dark as a dungeon way up in the air

G   C   G
Come gather 'round me you little monkeys and a story I'll tell
                                       D   G
About a brave young primate, outer space knew him well
                                  C   G
He was born at the top of a big old tree
                           D   G
Way back in Nineteen and Fifty-Three

G   C   G
He could swing through the jungle and hang by his toes
                                  D   G
'Til they took him to Russia cause they could I suppose
                            C   G
Dressed him up in a spacesuit and it started to snow
                              D   G
Shot him off in a rocket where no man would go

G   C   G
Space Monkey, Space Monkey, what you doing up there
                                       D   G
Why it's dark as a dungeon way up in the air
                                              C   G
There'll be no one to greet you when you get back home
                              D   G
No hammer, no sickle you'll be all on your own

G   C   G
He had plenty of Cuban bananas and loads of Spam
                                       D   G
But he found great difficulty trying to open the can
                                              C   G
One day he slipped on a banana peel and the ship lost control
                           D   G
It spun out of orbit and shot out the black hole
                                  C   G
It's been four decades now, that's nine monkey years
                                              D   G
That's a long time for a Space Monkey to confront all his fears

G   C   G
Space Monkey, Space Monkey, what you doing up there
                                       D   G
Why it's dark as a dungeon way up in the air
                                              C   G
There'll be no one to greet you when you get back home
                              D   G
No hammer, no sickle you'll be all on your own

G   C   G
Space Monkey, Space Monkey, it's time to get real
                                       D   G
The space race is over, how does it feel
                                              C   G
Cold War's had a heat wave, Iron Curtain's torn down
                                       D   G
They've rolled up the carpet in Space Monkey town

G   C   G
Now Leningrad is Petersburg and Petersburg's hell
                                       D   G
For a card-carrying monkey with a story to tell

The Space Monkey was reportedly last sighted
            C   G
about a half a block off of Red Square
                                                     D   G
In a karaoke bar having a few drinks with some of his friends

G   C
There was the dog that flew Sputnik and a blind
                  G
Red-headed, one-legged parrot
                                                     D   G
Who had done some minor research for Dow Chemical

They were drinking American Vodka imported
C   G
All the way from Paducah, Kentucky

And reportedly had their arms
                                              (Break)
Around each other's shoulders singing

"Those were the days, my friend, we thought they'd never end"

G   C   G
Space Monkey, Space Monkey, there's nothing to do
                                       D   G
But it's better than living in a Communist zoo
                                              C   G
There'll be no one to greet you when you get back home
                              D   G
No hammer or sickle you'll be all on your own

SPACE MONKEY

GATHER Round Me
You Monkeys
AND A story I'll Tell
ABOUT A BRAVE YOUNG
PRIMATE
OUTER SPACE KNEW
HIM WELL

He was born at the Top
of a Big old Tree
way back in 19and 53
He swung thru the jungle
and away by his Toes
Till they took him to
Russia

Cause they could I suppose

They dressed him in
a spacesuit
and it's total to snow
and They shot him in
a Rocket
Where no man
would Go

SPANISH PIPEDREAM

Written by John Prine

```
              G                            C
She was a level-headed dancer on the road to alcohol
       D7                              G
And I was just a soldier on my way to Montreal

Well she pressed her chest against me
            C
About the time the jukebox broke
          D7
Yeah she gave me a peck on the back of the neck
                          G
And these are the words she spoke

              G
Blow up your TV, throw away your paper
          D                G
Go to the country, build you a home

Plant a little garden, eat a lot of peaches
            D          G  D  G
Try and find Jesus on your own

       G                    C
Well I sat there at the table and I acted real naive
      D7                              G
For I knew that topless lady had something up her sleeve

Well she danced around the bar room
          C
And she did the hoochy-coo
          D7
Yeah she sang her song all night long
                 G
Telling me what to do
```

```
              G
Blow up your TV, throw away your paper
          D                G
Go to the country, build you a home

Plant a little garden, eat a lot of peaches
            D          G  D  G
Try and find Jesus on your own

       G                          C
Well I was young and hungry and about to leave that place
          D7                              G
When just as I was leaving, well she looked me in the face

I said, "You must know the answer"
              C
She said, "No but I'll give it a try"
          D7
And to this very day we've been living our way
                      G
Here is the reason why

              G
We blew up our TV, threw away our paper
          D                G
Went to the country, built us a home

Had a lot of children, fed 'em on peaches
            D          G  D  G
They all found Jesus on their own
```

This is 1973 or '74 when we played the Opry House in Nashville. Bonnie headlined, I was in the middle, and Tom opened. We look like an ad for a thrift store.

SPEED OF THE SOUND OF LONELINESS

Written by John Prine

G   C
You come home late and you come home early
D   G
You come on big when you're feeling small
                                   C
You come home straight and you come home curly
D   G
Sometimes you don't come home at all

G   C
So what in the world's come over you
D   G
And what in Heaven's name have you done
                                   C
You've broken the speed of the sound of loneliness
D   G
You're out there running just to be on the run

G   C
Well I got a heart that burns with a fever
D   G
And I got a worried and a jealous mind
                             C
Well how can a love that'll last forever
D   G
Get left so far behind

G   C
So what in the world's come over you
D   G
And what in Heaven's name have you done
                                   C
You've broken the speed of the sound of loneliness
D   G
You're out there running just to be on the run

G   C
It's a mighty mean and a dreadful sorrow
D   G
That's crossed the evil line today
                             C
Well how can you ask about tomorrow
D   G
When we ain't got one word to say

G   C
So what in the world's come over you
D   G
And what in Heaven's name have you done
                                 C
You've broken the speed of the sound of loneliness
D   G
You're out there running just to be on the run

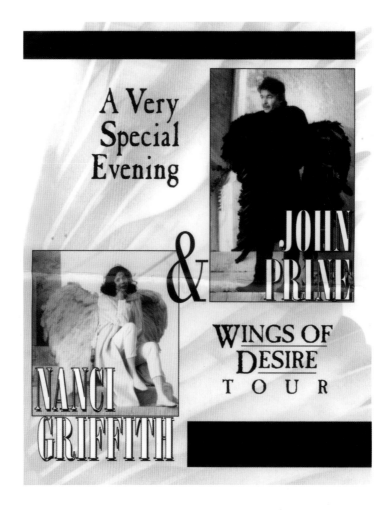

Boy these guys sure are great. The best guitarist and bass player ever to pick up the instruments in the whole world. I mean really THE absolute best. I am going to give them both a big fat raise.

"...Wheels of automobiles moving along through the drifting snow..." All of that came from looking out my bedroom window in the house where I grew up.

JUL 67

STORM WINDOWS

Written by John Prine

G
I can hear the wheels of the automobiles
   C   D   G
So far away just moving along through the drifting snow

It's times like these when the temperatures freeze
C   D   G
I sit alone just looking at the world through a storm window
Cm   G
And down on the beach the sandman sleeps
Cm   G
Time don't fly, it bounds and leaps
Cm   G
And a country band that plays for keeps
                  D
They play it so slow

G   **C**   **D**
Don't let your baby down
G   **C**   **D**
Don't let your baby down
G   **C**   **D G C G D**
Don't let your baby down

          G
Well, the spirits were high 'til the well went dry
C   D   G
For so long the raven at my window was only a crow

I bought the rights to the inside fights
C   D   G
And watched a man just beating his hand against a storm window
Cm   G
While miles away o'er hills and streams
Cm   G
A candle burns a witch's dreams
Cm   G
And silence is golden 'til it screams
                  D
Right through your bones

G   **C**   **D**
Don't let your baby down
G   **C**   **D**
Don't let your baby down
G   **C**   **D G C G D**
Don't let your baby down

D   *C*   *G*
Storm windows, gee but I'm getting old
D   *A*   *D*
Storm windows, keep away the cold

G
I can hear the wheels of the automobiles
          C   D   G
So far away just moving along through the drifting snow

It's times like these when the temperatures freeze
C   D   G
I sit alone just looking at the world through a storm window
Cm   G
And down on the beach the sandman sleeps
Cm   G
Time don't fly, it bounds and leaps
Cm   G
And a country band that plays for keeps
                  D
They play it so slow

G   **C**   **D**
Don't let your baby down
G   **C**   **D**
Don't let your baby down
G   **C**   **D G C G D**
Don't let your baby down

SWEET REVENGE

Written by John Prine

G
I got kicked off Noah's Ark
      C   G
I turn my cheek to unkind remarks
                               D
There was two of everything but one of me
                  G
And when the rains came tumbling down
       C   G
I held my breath and I stood my ground
                  D   C G
And I watched that ship go sailing out to sea

       C
Take it back, take it back
  G
Oh no you can't say that
                      D
All of my friends are not dead or in jail
G
Through rock and through stone
    C   G
The black wind still moans
                 D   C G
Sweet revenge, sweet revenge without fail

         G
I caught an aisle seat on a plane
          C   G
And drove an English teacher half insane
                                  D
Making up jokes about bicycle spokes and red balloons
     G
So I called up my local deejay
       C   G
And he didn't have a lot to say
                  D   C   G
But the radio has learned all of my favorite tunes

         C
Take it back, take it back
  G
Oh no you can't say that
                      D
All of my friends are not dead or in jail
G
Through rock and through stone
    C   G
The black wind still moans
                 D   C G
Sweet revenge, sweet revenge without fail

         G
The white meat is on the run
        C   G
And the dark meat is far too done
                            D
And the milkman left me a note yesterday
        G
Get out of this town by noon
       C   G
You're coming on way too soon
                    D   C G
And besides that we never liked you anyway

         C
Take it back, take it back
  G
Oh no you can't say that
                      D
All of my friends are not dead or in jail
G
Through rock and through stone
    C   G
The black wind still moans
                 D   C G
Sweet revenge, sweet revenge without fail

This is from the Village Voice. Bonnie and I had just met. She was playing down the street at the Gaslight.

vis and Shook for a building treatment of "Gypsy Woman," a pop oldie. Comments by Travis add to the set's fun, but his delivery suffers from lack of clarity. The final medley is a flashy peak as the duo does an overly-rapid Beatles medley, including "Lady Madonna," "Back in the USSR," and "Nowhere Man," whose sprint speed is a comic gem. The boys have been developing their act for about three years in the New England area. They are ready to branch out.

Kirb.

TOM PRINE
Songs
40 Mins.
Bitter End, New York

Tom Prine, a young Chicago-based folksinger, whose compositions are being done by Kris Kristofferson, John Denver and others, has brought his unusual songs to the Bitter End. His straightforward delivery cannot mask his humorous lyrics any more than his humorous lyrics can mask his potent messages.

Prine, whose first album is just out on Atlantic, opens with "Illegal Smile," one of his numbers that's picked up by other performers, but his message really becomes clear with "Your Flag Decal Won't Get You Into Heaven Anymore." His point, with his usual tongue in cheek, is that there isn't anymore room because of war deaths.

"Sam Stone" is a powerful tale of an ex-soldier with the dope habit, "Spanish Pipedream," with a touch of country, is a light number about chucking it all for a woman and a home in the country. Prine accompanies himself on guitar, which is strictly rhythmic

a new locally produced tv show "Some of My Best Friends," 7:30 p.m.

Now, he has turned to night clubs and it is difficult to properl appraise him since everything h did was funny with the crow roaring at every line, new and ol He got started off right by havin Regis Philbin introduce him b phone and he took over from there fracturing the audience fo a solid 20 minutes and when h had run out of all his topical lines and clever jokes, he stepped righ to the microphone and got a tre mendous mitt singing "Second Time Around."

Lit.

BONNIE RAITT (3)
Songs
35 Mins.
Gaslight II, New York

Bonnie Raitt, the daughter o John Raitt, is a young folk and blues singer with an easy natura presence and at Gaslight II, she shows herself quite a performers with good voice, exceptional interpretations, and good guitar style.

Miss Raitt, whose debut album on Warner Bros. is due this month, begins with a strong blues in "Mighty Tight Woman." In addition to her firstrate acoustic guitar work, the musianship of her supporting musicians, Eric Caz, harmonica, and a bass guitarist known only as Freebo, soon is apparent.

She also takes a turn on an old steel-base guitar in bottleneck style for "Louisiana Blues," an uptempo number that is a wow. Another top uptempo tune is Stephen Stills' "Bluebird." A beauty in a tender vein is her own "Thank You."

In the show caught, Mississippi Fred MacDowell, also on the bill, joined Miss Raitt, Caz and Freebo, taking vocals in "Gonna Buy Me a

TAKING A WALK
Written by John Prine and Pat McLaughlin

```
G                Bm   C   D           G  Bm  C  D
A man came to our house, I believe it was yesterday
            G          Bm C  D          G  Bm  C  D
I would have invited him in but I didn't have a lot to say
B7                    Em
His anticipation of me opening the door
   B7                           Em
Outweighed my apprehension as it never had before
    B7                      Em                    C  D
And drove my concentration right through that hardwood floor
```

```
         G  Bm   C   D
I'm taking a walk
         G  Bm   C   D
I'm going outside
         G  Bm   C   D
I'm taking a walk
          G  Bm   C   D
I'm just getting by
```

```
G                    Bm  C D            G  Bm  C D
There's a girl in the white house, I don't even know her name
G          Bm  C      D              G  Bm  C  D
Her disheveled appearance speaks volumes of shame
B7                              Em
It's an embarrassing situation, but a situation just the same
   B7                          Em
The way she walks on others and never takes the blame
   B7                 Em                  C  D
Upsets my constitution beyond its mortal frame
```

```
         G  Bm   C   D
I'm taking a walk
         G  Bm   C   D
I'm going outside
         G  Bm   C   D
I'm watching the birds
         G  Bm   C   D
I'm just getting by
```

```
G                    Bm   C    D         G  Bm   C  D
Found a card in the pocket of my worn out overalls
G                     Bm   C    D         G  Bm   C  D
From a girl in Cedar Rapids now residing in Idaho Falls
B7                                           Em
I wish you could have been there when she opened up the door
     B7                          Em
And looked me in the face like she never did before
   B7                     Em                    C  D
I felt about as welcome as a Wal-Mart Superstore
```

```
         G  Bm   C   D
I'm taking a walk
         G  Bm   C   D
I'm going outside
         G  Bm   C   D
I'm taking a walk
          G  Bm   C   D
I don't need a ride
          G  Bm   C   D
I'm watching the birds
         G  Bm   C   D
Flying so high
```

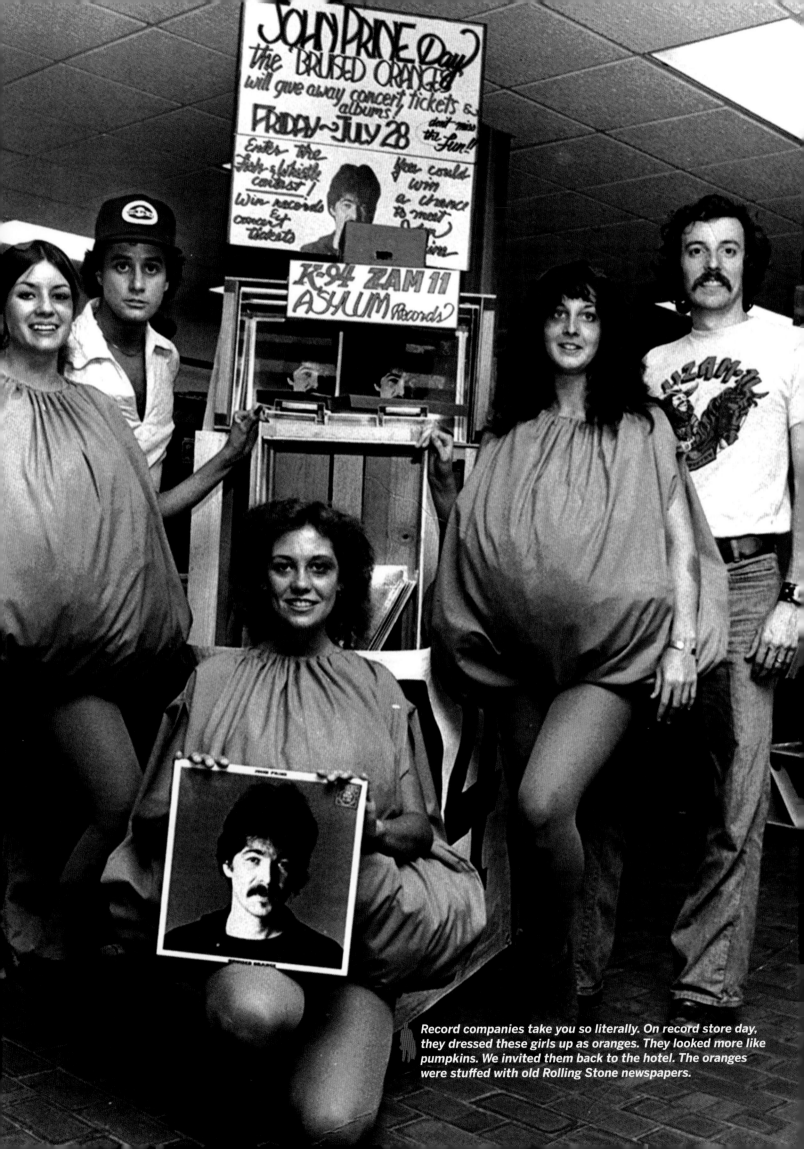

Record companies take you so literally. On record store day, they dressed these girls up as oranges. They looked more like pumpkins. We invited them back to the hotel. The oranges were stuffed with old Rolling Stone newspapers.

THAT'S THE WAY THE WORLD GOES 'ROUND

Written by John Prine

Capo on 5th Fret

C
I know a guy that's got a lot to lose
      F
He's a pretty nice fellow but he's kind of confused
        C
He's got muscles in his head that ain't never been used
               G7
Thinks he owns half of this town
C
Starts drinking heavy gets a big red nose
F
Beats his old lady with a rubber hose
        C
Then he takes her out to dinner and buys her new clothes
      G   C
That's the way that the world goes 'round

C
That's the way that the world goes 'round
      F
You're up one day, the next you're down
    C
It's half an inch of water and you think you're gonna drown
      G   **C**
That's the way that the world goes 'round

C
I was sitting in the bathtub counting my toes
      F
When the radiator broke, water all froze
        C
I got stuck in the ice without my clothes
               G7
Naked as the eyes of a clown
        C
I was crying ice cubes hoping I'd croak
        F
When the sun come through the window, the ice all broke
    C
I stood up and laughed thought it was a joke
      G   C
That's the way that the world goes 'round

C
That's the way that the world goes 'round
      F
You're up one day, the next you're down
    C
It's half an inch of water and you think you're gonna drown
          G   **C**
That's the way that the world goes 'round

THE BOTTOMLESS LAKE

Written by John Prine

Capo on 3rd Fret

```
         G                               D          G
Here's the story of a man and his family and a big trip that they took
                                          A          D
Well I heard all about in a restaurant and I read it in a history book
  C                 G                           C
They rented a car at the Erie Canal but the car didn't have no brake
                    G              D           G    C G D G
Said Ma to Pa, "My God this car is gonna fall into the Bottomless Lake"

   G                                  D             G
Well Mama turned to Daddy with a pale face said, "I've done something horribly wrong
                                          A                  D
Well the waters still runnin' in the bathtub and I think I left the kitchen light on"
    C              G                  G                      C
Then I heard a crash the car went splash and the compass rolled around and around
    C          G          D         G
Oh for Heaven's sake, we fell in a lake and I think we're all gonna drown

    D                                  G
We are falling down, down to the bottom of a hole in the ground
                        C                   G
Smoke 'em if you got 'em, I'm so scared I can hardly breathe
      D                    G   C G D G
I may never see my sweetheart again

         G                          D             G
There was plenty of food in the backseat and the windows was rolled up tight
                             A                  D
So we all nibbled on a chicken leg, told stories way through the night
  C              G                      C
Well Pa told one that he told before and the baby got a bellyache
                    G         D              G
Said Ma to Pa, "My God this car is falling down the Bottomless Lake"

    D                                  G
We are falling down, down to the bottom of a hole in the ground
                        C                   G
Smoke 'em if you got 'em, I'm so scared I can hardly breathe
      D                    G   C G D G
I may never see my sweetheart again

G                         D              G
Papa played the music on the radio, Mama rocked the baby to sleep
                                       A                    D
He said he would've taken the other road but he didn't think the lake was that deep
    C              G                          C
Well if the ferry been there at the end of the pier, we'd be half way to Uncle Jake's
                         G              D              G
Instead of looking at fish out the window I wish, we'd hit the bottom of the Bottomless Lake
```

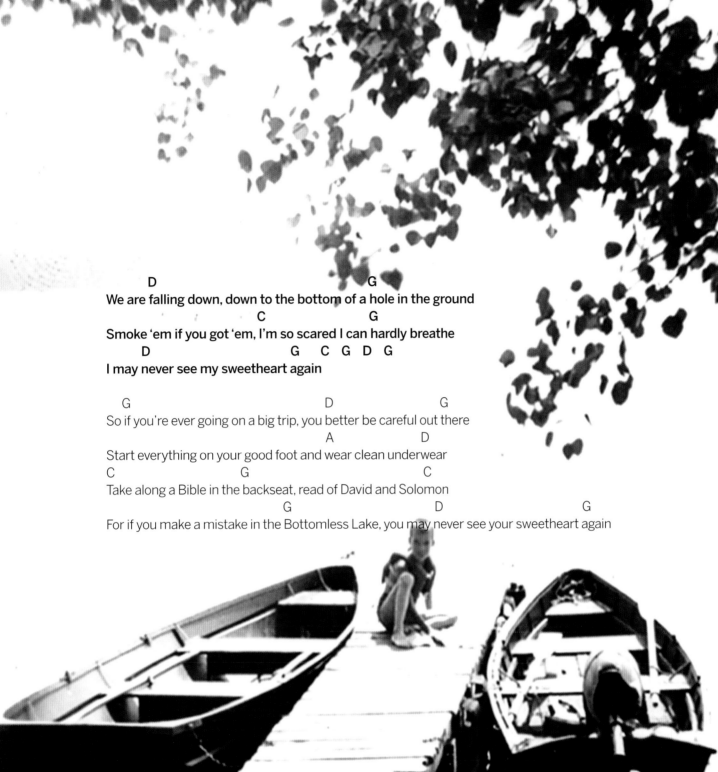

<pre>
      D   G
We are falling down, down to the bottom of a hole in the ground
                              C   G
Smoke 'em if you got 'em, I'm so scared I can hardly breathe
      D   G   C G D G
I may never see my sweetheart again

  G   D   G
So if you're ever going on a big trip, you better be careful out there
                              A   D
Start everything on your good foot and wear clean underwear
C   G   C
Take along a Bible in the backseat, read of David and Solomon
                        G   D   G
For if you make a mistake in the Bottomless Lake, you may never see your sweetheart again
</pre>

I took this guitar to a guy to put the coon rod on the headstock. I'd bring a six pack of beer when I'd go to see him and we'd talk about stuff. I didn't want the guitar to be done. So I said, "Why don't you put a heart up here with an arrow through it?" It took him six months to do that. I kept coming down to check on him and bringing beer. I never wanted to put my name on the neck of a guitar because I can't play above the 3rd fret. But I said, "Wouldn't it be proper if my name was somewhere between a perpetual hard on and a broken heart?" He agreed.

BORN SCHOOL HOBBY'S ADRESS PHONE

HI MY NAME IS JOHN PRINE, I AM 23 YRS OLD I
PROVISO EAST HIGH SCHOOL IN 1964 AND WENT T
        I SPENT 1966 &1967 IN THE ARMY IN GERMA
AND ATTENDED CAREER ACADAMY'S SCHOOL OF FAM
OF BROADCASTING   . ~~FOR EXAMPLE SOME OF MY~~
~~SPORTING EVENTS~~   aMONG MY MANY ASSIGNMENT
A LARGE MM LOCAL SOCIAL EVENT .. ... PLAYING
PREFORMED FOR SIZABLE AUDIENCES ON STRICTLY
A HOBBY..... IHAVE CHOSEN BROADCASTING AS A
REFLECT THE LIFE IN THESE INTERESTING TIMES
LIKE TO BE APART OF YOU NEWS STAFF BUT I AM
OPEN THANKS TO MY FINE TRAINING AT CAREER AC
OF HUMOR AND IAM HONEST.. I BELIEVE I COULD
MY SERVICES FOR I PLAN TO LOOK AT BROADCASTI
THANK YOU FOR YOUR TIME...

BORN IN MELROSE PARK ILL.. I GRADUATED H,,
RK FOR T HE POST OFFICE SHORTLY THERE AFTER
,,AFTER MY RELEASE I RETURNED TO THE POST OFFICE
BROADCASTING WHERE I WAS TRAINED IN ALL ASPECT:
~~SIGNMENTS WERE COVERING LIVE EVENTS SUCH AS~~
ERE LIVE COVERAGE OF SPORTS AND I ALSO COVERED
GUITAR AND WRITING SONGS ARE MY HOBBYS,, I HAVE
AMATEUR BASIS.. I ALSO ENJOY CREATIVE WRITING AS
ER BECAUSE OF THE WAY TELAVISION AND RADIO
WHICH WE LIVE .. IT IS ALSO THEE REASON I WOULD
SIT LE ENOUGH TO ENTER INTO ANY FIELD THAT IS
MY. I ALSO MIGHT ADD THAT I'M HAVE A GOOD SENS
AN ASSET TO YOUR STATION IF YOU DECIDE TO EMPLO
AS A WAY OF LIFE RATHER THAN JUST A JOB .....

I wanted to be a radio journalist. I said I performed on an amateur basis - in other words, no one was looking at me. An honest PS would have read: I'll do anything! All I'm looking for is a place to play my songs for somebody!

THE GREAT COMPROMISE
Written by John Prine

Capo on 5th Fret

G
I knew a girl who was almost a lady
       C   G
She had a way with all the men in her life
     D
Every inch of her blossomed in beauty
          C   G
And she was born on the Fourth of July

Well she lived in an aluminum house trailer
       C   G
And she worked in a jukebox saloon
       D
And she spent all the money that I give her
    C   G
Just to see the old man in the moon

G
I used to sleep at the foot of Old Glory
   C   **G**
And awake in the dawn's early light
      C   **G**
But much to my surprise when I opened my eyes
       D   **G**
I was a victim of the Great Compromise

G
Well we'd go out on Saturday evenings
    C   G
To the drive-in on Route Forty-One
      D
And it was there that I first suspected
           C   G
That she was doing what she'd already done

She said, "Johnny won't you get me some popcorn"
       C   G
And she knew I had to walk pretty far
      D
And as soon as I passed through the moonlight
       C   G
She hopped into a foreign sports car

G
I used to sleep at the foot of Old Glory
   C   **G**
And awake in the dawn's early light
      C   **G**
But much to my surprise when I opened my eyes
       D   **G**
I was a victim of the Great Compromise

G
Well you know I could have beat up that fellow
        C   G
But it was her that had hopped into his car
      D
Many times I'd fought to protect her
        C   G
But this time she was going too far

Now some folks they call me a coward
        C   G
Cause I left her at the drive-in that night
      D
But I'd rather have names thrown at me
       C   G
Than to fight for a thing that ain't right

G
I used to sleep at the foot of Old Glory
   C   **G**
And awake in the dawn's early light
      C   **G**
But much to my surprise when I opened my eyes
       D   **G**
I was a victim of the Great Compromise

G
Well she writes all the fellows love letters
       C   G
Saying, "Greetings, come and see me real soon"
      D
And they go and line up in the barroom
          C   G
And spend the night in that sick woman's room

But sometimes I get awful lonesome
       C   G
And I wish she was my girl instead
      D
But she won't let me live with her
       C   G
And she makes me live in my head

G
I used to sleep at the foot of Old Glory
   C   **G**
And awake in the dawn's early light
      C   **G**
But much to my surprise when I opened my eyes
       D   **G**
I was a victim of the Great Compromise

THE LATE JOHN GARFIELD BLUES

Written by John Prine

```
G                                        C            G
Black faces pressed against the glass where rain has pressed its weight
                                 A            D
Wind blown scarves in top down cars all share one western trait
C       D       G                        B7           C
Sadness leaks through tear-stained cheeks from winos to dime store Jews
                     G          D7          G
Probably don't know they gave me these late John Garfield blues


G                                        C            G
Midnight fell on Franklin Street and the lamppost bulbs were broke
                                 A            D
For the life of me I could not see but I heard a brand new joke
    C       D       G                B7                  C
Two men were standing upon a bridge, one jumped and screamed, "You lose"
                     G          D7          G
And just left the odd man holding those late John Garfield blues


D
An old man sleeps with his conscience at night
G
Young kids sleep with their dreams
         A
While the mentally ill sit perfectly still
                  D
And live through life's in-betweens


    G                        C            G
I'm going away to the last resort in a week or two real soon
                                 A            D
Where the fish don't bite but once a night by the cold light of the moon
    C       D       G                        B7           C
The horses scream, the nightmare's dream and the dead men all wear shoes
                     G          D7          G
Cause everybody's dancing those late John Garfield blues
```

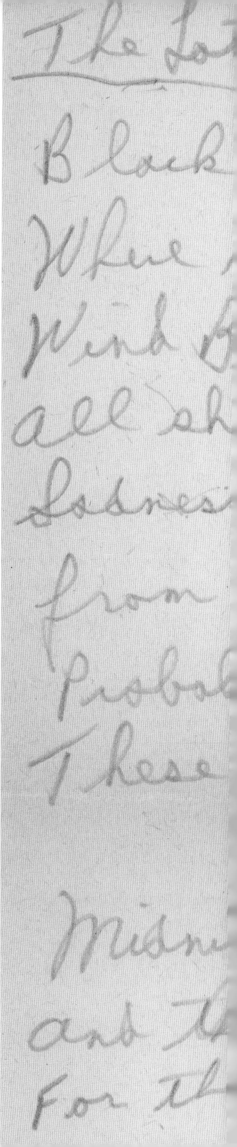

This song is on Diamonds in the Rough. Kris Kristofferson got an early copy on acetate before it came out. Rita Coolidge and Kris had just married and moved into a house on Franklin St. in LA. There was no furniture but they borrowed a record player. They were sitting around on boxes listening to the record, when I got to the part "...midnight fell on Franklin Street," the electricity went out in the house. Later, they found out that at one time John Garfield had lived there. I just wrote ,"Franklin Street" because it sounded good. When you write a song, you don't know what ghosts are going to come out of it.

John Garfield Blues

Faces pressed against the glass
in has pressed its weight
own scarves in top down ca
z one western trait
leaks thru tear stained che
nos to Dimestore Jews
don't know they gave me
ate John Garfield blues.

t fell on Franklin street
lampost bulbs were broke
life of me, I could not see

THE OLDEST BABY IN THE WORLD
Written by John Prine and Donnie Fritts

```
C                                    F                 C
She's got the mind of a child and a body peaking over the hill
                                     D7              G
Well she would if she could and she should but nobody will
       F                                    C   G/B  Am
With her nails painted red and her hair so unnaturally curled
       F                    G            C
Well I think that she may be the oldest baby in the world

C                                    F                 C
She's tasted the nightlife but it's left her with nothing but hunger
                                     D7                      G
And all the available men seem to think that they want something younger
       F                                    C   G/B  Am
But youth is a costume and the beauty within lies unfurled
       F                    G            C
And I think that she may be the oldest baby in the world

         F                                                        C
Fast horses win races and royal flushes beat aces and everyone's playing to keep
         D                              G
So let's turn out the lights and rock that old baby to sleep

             C                      F                 C
She loves the sound of the rain but you know she's still afraid of the thunder
                                     D7              G
She keeps a head full of hope and a heart that's so full of wonder
       F                                    C   G/B  Am
She may look like a woman but she's still some daddy's little girl
       F                    G            C
And I think that she may be the oldest baby in the world
```

THE SINS OF MEMPHISTO

Written by John Prine

Capo on 3rd Fret

```
A        D              A
From the bells of St. Mary's to the Count of Monte Cristo
E                                          D              A
Nothing can stop, nothing can stop, nothing can stop the sins of Memphisto
```

```
E                        D
Sally used to play with her hula hoops, now she tells her problems to therapy groups
E                              D
Grandpa's on the front lawn staring at a rake, wondering if his marriage was a terrible mistake
   E                             D                            A
I'm sitting on the front steps drinking orange crush, wondering if it's possible for me still blush, uh huh oh yeah
```

```
   E                    D
A boy on a bike with corduroy slacks sleeps in the river by the railroad tracks
E                            D                            A
Waits for the whistle on the train to scream, so he can close his eyes and begin to dream, uh huh oh yeah
```

```
A        D              A
From the bells of St. Mary's to the Count of Monte Cristo
E                                          D              A
Nothing can stop, nothing can stop, nothing can stop the sins of Memphisto
```

```
    E                              D
The hands on his watch spin slowly around, with his mind on a bus that goes all over town
E                              D
Looking at the babies and the factories and listening to the music of Mister Squeeze
   E                           D                          A
As if by magic or remote control, he finds a piece of a puzzle that he missed in his soul, uh huh oh yeah
```

```
A        D              A
From the bells of St. Mary's to the Count of Monte Cristo
E                                          D              A
Nothing can stop, nothing can stop, nothing can stop the sins of Memphisto
```

```
E                        D
Adam and Eve and Lucy and Ricky bit the big apple and got a little sticky
   E                              D
Esmeralda and the Hunchback of Notre Dame, they humped each other like they had no shame
    E                              D                          A
They paused as they posed for a Polaroid photo, she whispered in his ear, "Exactlyodo, Quasimodo"
```

```
A        D              A
From the bells of St. Mary's to the Count of Monte Cristo
E                                          D              A
Nothing can stop, nothing can stop, nothing can stop the sins of Memphisto
```

```
E                        D                            A
Sally used to play with her hula hoops, now she tells her problems to therapy groups, uh huh oh yeah
```

Adam + Eve + Lucy + Ricky
sat the Big apple.
and all got a flickey
From The Tips of their Toes
To The Bottom of Their ~~then~~ See

"Esmarelda and The Hunchback
of Notre Dame.
Kissed While He Hung his head
in Shame
Then They went to the airport
and got Themselves a Photo
and She whispered in his Ear.
Exactly, do Quasimodo

2ND Verse

There She Goes

There She Goes
I thought she'd never leave
Heaven Knows
She sure gives me the creeps
You know I loved that woman
to the power of Height
We both got jivin fever
screwed our heads uptite
Then it came to Blows
Hey Hey   Hey Hey
There she Goes

There She Goes
Just a walkin down the street
I suppose
The next fellow that she meets
Should have her head examined
By an X ray machine
So he can see those pictures
That I've already seen
Just so he knows
Hey Hey   Hey Hey
There She goes

THERE SHE GOES

Written by John Prine

```
E                                                  A
Hey there she goes, well I thought she'd never leave, Heaven knows
                                                   E
You know it sure gives me the creeps, you know I went and loved that woman

To the power of height, we both got jiving fever, screwed our heads uptight
              B7                                E
Then it came to blows, hey, hey, hey, hey, hey, hey there she goes, hey there she goes

E                                            A
Hey there she goes, just a walking down the street I suppose
                                    E
The next fellow that she meets should have her head examined

By an x-ray machine, so he can see all of those pictures that I've already seen
         B7                              E
Just so he knows, hey, hey, hey, hey, hey, hey there she goes, hey there she goes

E7       A                                                    E
Well there must be something somewhere that makes me want to hurt myself inside
                A                                      B7
Yeah we were regular Doctor Jekyll but together we were Mister and Misses Hyde
                        E
What a rough, rough ride

E                                          A
Hey there she goes, she's walking out on me with all her clothes
                                  E
Looking fine as she could be, well I seen her on down at the courthouse

I was sober as the judge, we tried to talk things over but the grudge just wouldn't budge
       B7                              E
I said adios, hey, hey, hey, hey, hey, hey there she goes, hey there she goes

E7       A                                                    E
Well there must be something somewhere that makes me want to hurt myself inside
                A                                      B7
Yeah we were regular Doctor Jekyll but together we were Mister and Misses Hyde
                        E
What a rough, rough ride

E                                                  A
Hey there she goes, well I thought she'd never leave, Heaven knows
                                                   E
You know it sure gives me the creeps, you know I went and loved that woman

To the power of height, we both got jiving fever, screwed our heads uptight
              B7                                E
Then it came to blows, hey, hey, hey, hey, hey, hey there she goes
```

UNWED FATHERS

Written by John Prine and Bobby Braddock

G   C   G
In an Appalachian Greyhound station
C   G   D   G
She sits there waiting in a family way
                C   G
"Goodbye Brother, tell Mom I love her
C   G   D   G
Tell all the others I'll write someday"

G   C   G
From a teenage lover to an unwed mother
                       D
Kept undercover like some bad dream
              G   C   G
While unwed fathers, they can't be bothered
C   G   D   G
They run like water through a mountain stream

G   C   G
In a cold and gray town a nurse says, "Lay down
C   G   D   G
This ain't no playground and this ain't home"
C   G
Someone's children out having children
C   G   D G
In a gray stone building all alone

G   C   G
From a teenage lover to an unwed mother
                       D
Kept undercover like some bad dream
              G   C   G
While unwed fathers, they can't be bothered
C   G   D   G
They run like water through a mountain stream

G   C   G
On a somewhere else bound Smoky Mountain Greyhound
C   G   D   G
She bows her head down humming lullabies
                  C   G
"Your Daddy never meant to hurt you ever
C   G   D   G
He just don't live here but you've got his eyes"

G   C   G
From a teenage lover to an unwed mother
                       D
Kept undercover like some bad dream
              G   C   G
While unwed fathers, they can't be bothered
C   G   D   G
They run like water through a mountain stream

~~Half~~ any where but here
'on a Somewhere Else Bound
SMOKY MOUNTAIN
Allegany Greyhound

.seen You

~~I guess~~ Lean To
~~He didn't~~ Mean To

SAW you thru

.maw Too

Some Boys don't
mean to
Do The Things that They
~~I Do~~ ~~thought~~ ~~Why its~~ ~~He's never~~ do
ever!

Some bastard stole that guitar. At the end of the tour it never made it home. I had it for little over a year. It looked like a brand new Oldsmobile, like it had white walls. It makes me sad to look at this picture now. But it really makes me sad to see me wearing suspenders.

Sitting on my bunk in the barracks, in Germany, playing my Gibson Hummingbird. My Dad shipped it over to me. That's my buddy Arnie, from the song "Pretty Good," where I sing "...I got a friend in Fremont..." I'd just sing for the guys. They always wanted to hear me play. They all liked country music except for Arnie, he thought it was corny. I was writing songs in the Army, but I was just singing the songs I'd learned to sing for my Dad.

WAY BACK THEN

Written by John Prine

```
G                                    C
Night is falling, we're doing the things we do
D7                                        G
You are acting just like me, I'm acting just like you
                                     C
Do you remember when you were my friend
D7                                   G
That's the way I'd like things, just like way back then


G                             C
Baby's sleeping, brother is on the run
D7                              G
I am out undoing all the good I've done
                                        C
If you loved me, tell you what I would do
D7                                          G
I'd wrap the world in silver foil, bring it home to you


G                        C
Lately I see that I can't pretend
D7                              G
I may never ever see the likes of you again
                                       C
I take a walk, I come back home, then I sit a spell
D7                                        G
Watch the ponies dance around the empty wishing well


G                                 C
Night has fallen, I've said the things I did
D7                              G
The only baby sleeping is when I was a kid
                                     C
Do you remember when you were my friend
D7                                    G
That's the way I'd like things just like way back then
```

YES I GUESS THEY OUGHTA NAME A DRINK AFTER YOU

Written by John Prine

```
A                              D
Oh I get drunk most every night, seems like all we do is fight
    A                       E
The more I drink, the less I feel blue
      A                           D
Sometimes I feel like an awful fool, spending my life on an old bar stool
     A              E                      A
And yes I guess they oughta name a drink after you


A                              D
If this date were to be our last, I'd never sit down this glass
    A                                  E
It'd take all the booze in the world to forget you
      A                         D
You've left my heart a vacant lot, I'll fill it with another shot
     A              E                      A
And yes I guess they oughta name a drink after you


A                  D
Looks like I had my fill, guess I better pay my bill
      A                            E
When I started out I only meant to have a few
     A                          D
Someone just said that you left town, I better get a double round
     A              E                      A
And yes I guess they oughta name a drink after you
```

YOU GOT GOLD

Written by John Prine and Keith Sykes

Capo on 2nd Fret

G   D
Is there ever enough space between us to keep us both honest and true
                                                            G
Why is it so hard just to sit in the yard and stare at the sky so blue
                                                               C
I've got a new way of walking and a new way of talking, honey when I'm around you
                                    G   D   G
But it gives me the blues, when I've got some good news and you're not there to bring it to

G   D
Life is a blessin', it's a delicatessen of all the little favors you do
                                                            G
All wrapped up together no matter the weather, baby you always come through
                                                            C
It's a measure of treasure that gives me the pleasure of loving you the way I do
                                    G   D   G
And you know I would gladly say I need your love badly and bring these little things to you

                            C   G
Cause you got gold, gold inside of you
                  C   G
You got gold, gold inside of you
                      D   G
Well I got some gold inside me too

G   D
Well I'm thinking I'm knowing that I gotta be going, you know I hate to say so long
                                                            G
It gives me an ocean of mixed up emotion, I'll have to work it out in a song
                                                       C
Well I'm leaving a lot for the little I got, but you know a lot a little will do
                                  G   D   G
And if you give me your love, I'll let it shine up above and light my way back home to you

                            C   G
Cause you got gold, gold inside of you
                  C   G
You got gold, gold inside of you
                      D   G
Well I got some gold inside me too
                  C   G
You got wheels turning inside of you
                  C   G
You got wheels turning inside of you
                      D   G
Well I got wheels turning inside me too

YOUR FLAG DECAL WON'T GET YOU INTO HEAVEN ANYMORE

Written by John Prine

       G   C
While digesting Reader's Digest in the back of a dirty book store
 D   G
A plastic flag with gum on the back fell out on the floor

                               C
Well I picked it up and I ran outside, slapped it on my window shield
        D   G
And if I could see old Betsy Ross, I'd tell her how good I feel

        C   G
But your flag decal won't get you into Heaven anymore
       D   G
They're already overcrowded from your dirty little war
     C   G
Now Jesus don't like killing, no matter what the reason's for
       D   G   Bb C D
And your flag decal won't get you into Heaven anymore

       G   C
Well I went to the bank this morning and the cashier said to me
D   G
"If you join the Christmas club, we'll give you ten of them flags for free"
                              C
Well I didn't mess around a bit, I took him up on what he said
        D   G
And I stuck them stickers all over my car and one on my wife's forehead

        C   G
But your flag decal won't get you into Heaven anymore
       D   G
They're already overcrowded from your dirty little war
     C   G
Now Jesus don't like killing, no matter what the reason's for
       D   G   Bb C D
And your flag decal won't get you into Heaven anymore

       G   C
Well I got my window shield so filled with flags I couldn't see
       D   G
So I ran the car upside a curb and right into a tree
                               C
By the time they got a doctor down, I was already dead
       D   G
And I'll never understand why the man standing in the Pearly Gates said

        C   G
But your flag decal won't get you into Heaven anymore
       D   G
We're already overcrowded from your dirty little war
     C   G
Now Jesus don't like killing, no matter what the reason's for
       D   G   Bb C D
And your flag decal won't get you into Heaven anymore

A sense of humor defines John Prine

By ROBERT MARTIN

John Prine, who opened a one week stand last night at the Riverboat, has a quality seldom found in much of today's popular music, a sense of humor. Many singers can be amusing between numbers and Prine is no exception. He even made a joke out of as ancient a ritual as tuning his guitar. But in songs like Illegal Smile he takes what could have been a cliche-ridden paean to getting stoned and makes it an insanely logical result of a morning in which "A bowl of oatmeal tried to stare me down . . . and won."

His appearance on stage is that of a tousled-haired kid who just tumbled out of bed and found himself on stage. He shuffled around the stage wearing a bemused boyish grin and squinting into the spotlights. Many people in the audience were familiar with the words to his songs and sang along to tunes like Your Flag Decal Won't Get You Into Heaven Any More.

His voice has the gravel-like quality of having been filtered through old cigaret butts, and his guitar playing is basic chording with a country and western background. The lyrics are the important part and they are finely honed comments on life.

He occasionally deliberately juxtaposes cliche choruses like "Pretty good, It's alright, I can't complain" with original and unusual verses like one that concerned a woman who had a most unfortunate experience with a dog. The effect was humorous, ironic and well appreciated.

The self-deprecating tone that Prine takes in introducing many of his songs belies the seriousness of his treatment in actually singing them. It is obvious that we were witnessing an intelligent sensibility on display and that Prine, the owner, was a little nervous about laying his soul on his sleeve.

The kidding introduction to Sam Stone, a song about GI who returns from Vietnam with "A purple heart and a monkey on his back", could not hide the sadness and the touch of quiet anger that Prine showed in his singing.

An ability that Prine posseses that is very rare in young writers (he is 25) is that of being able to report sympathetically and convincingly about old people. In Hello in There he has written a pathetic and moving account of the loneliness of old age without ever stopping to condescension. When he had stopped singing it, there was an instant's hesitation before the applause as a mark of respect for that accomplishment. After all, one would hesitate before applauding a hymn.

Rolf Kempf, who played as second act to John Prine, demonstrated that he is an accomplished guitarist. He may also be an excellent lyricist, what was heard certainly was fine enough, but unfortunately Kempf mumbled away a goodly portion of his words. A couple of numbers, Bad Apple and Won't You Come See Me did survive and showed considerable promise.

Anything my brothers did, I thought, "That's my brother, I can do that too..." Doug was a gymnast so I had to become one. When I saw Dave playing the guitar, I learned it. I had no natural ability at either thing, but if I could picture myself doing it, I could do it, if I put enough work into it. That's why I said if my Dad liked ballet, I would have been Rudolph Nureyev. Shew, am I glad he didn't like ballet!

SONG CREDITS

Aimless Love • John Prine. Bruised Oranges (Admin. by Wixen Music Publishing Inc.) (ASCAP).

Ain't Hurtin' Nobody • John Prine. Weona Music (Admin. by Wixen Music Publishing Inc.) (BMI).

All The Best • John Prine. Weona Music (Admin. by Wixen Music Publishing Inc.) (BMI).

Angel From Montgomery • John Prine. WB Music Corp. o/b/o Walden Music (BMI).

Automobile • John Prine. Bruised Oranges (Admin. by Wixen Music Publishing Inc.) (ASCAP).

Blue Umbrella • John Prine. WB Music Corp. o/b/o Walden Music (BMI).

Bruised Orange (Chain Of Sorrow) • John Prine. Bruised Oranges (Admin. by Wixen Music Publishing Inc.) (ASCAP).

Christmas In Prison • John Prine. WB Music Corp. o/b/o Walden Music (BMI).

Common Sense • John Prine. WB Music Corp. o/b/o Walden Music (BMI).

Crazy As A Loon • John Prine; Pat McLaughlin. TommyJack Music (BMI); Corn Country Music (BMI).

Crooked Piece Of Time • John Prine. Bruised Oranges (Admin. by Wixen Music Publishing Inc.) (ASCAP).

Daddy's Little Pumpkin • John Prine; Pat McLaughlin. Weona Music (Admin. by Wixen Music Publishing Inc.) (BMI); Songs of Universal / Frankly Scarlett Music (BMI).

Dear Abby • John Prine. WB Music Corp. o/b/o Walden Music (BMI).

Donald And Lydia • . John Prine. WB Music Corp. o/b/o Walden Music (BMI).

Everything Is Cool • John Prine. Weona Music (Admin. by Wixen Music Publishing Inc.) (BMI).

Far From Me • John Prine. WB Music Corp. o/b/o Walden Music (BMI).

Fish And Whistle • John Prine. Bruised Oranges (Admin. by BMG Chrysalis) (ASCAP).

Glory Of True Love • John Prine; Roger Cook. TommyJack Music (BMI); Songs of Peer Int'l (ASCAP).

Grandpa Was A Carpenter • John Prine. WB Music Corp. o/b/o Walden Music (BMI).

Hello In There • John Prine. WB Music Corp. o/b/o Walden Music (BMI).

How Lucky • John Prine. Bruised Oranges (Admin. by Wixen Music Publishing Inc.) (ASCAP).

I Just Want To Dance With You • John Prine; Roger Cook. Bruised Oranges (Admin. by Wixen Music Publishing Inc.) (ASCAP); Roger Cook Music (PRS).

In Spite Of Ourselves • John Prine. Weona Music (Admin. by Wixen Music Publishing Inc.) (BMI).

It's A Big Old Goofy World • John Prine. Weona Music (Admin. by Wixen Music Publishing Inc.) (BMI).

Jesus The Missing Years • John Prine. Weona Music (Admin. by Wixen Music Publishing Inc.) (BMI).

Lake Marie • John Prine. Weona Music (Admin. by Wixen Music Publishing Inc.) (BMI).

Let's Talk Dirty In Hawaiian • John Prine; Fred Koller. Pink Sky Music (Admin. by Wixen Music Publishing Inc.) (BMI); Universal-Song of Polygram o/b/o Lucrative Music (BMI).

Linda Goes To Mars • John Prine. Bruised Oranges (Admin. by Wixen Music Publishing Inc.) (ASCAP).

Living In The Future • John Prine. Bruised Oranges (Admin. by Wixen Music Publishing Inc.) (ASCAP).

Long Monday • John Prine; Keith Sykes. TommyJack Music (BMI); Keith Sykes Music (BMI).

Love, Love, Love • John Prine; Keith Sykes. Bruised Oranges (Admin. by Wixen Music Publishing Inc.) (ASCAP); Keith Sykes Music (BMI).

Maureen, Maureen • John Prine. Bruised Oranges (Admin. by Wixen Music Publishing Inc.) (ASCAP).

Mexican Home • John Prine. WB Music Corp. o/b/o Walden Music (BMI).

One Red Rose • John Prine. Bruised Oranges (Admin. by Wixen Music Publishing Inc.) (ASCAP).

Only Love • John Prine; Roger Cook; Sandy Mason. Bruised Oranges (Admin. by Wixen Music Publishing Inc.) (ASCAP); Roger Cook Music (PRS); Good Music (ASCAP).

Paradise • John Prine. WB Music Corp. o/b/o Walden Music (BMI).

People Puttin' People Down • John Prine. Bruised Oranges (Admin. by Wixen Music Publishing Inc.) (ASCAP).

Picture Show • John Prine. Weona Music (Admin. by Wixen Music Publishing Inc.) (BMI).

Please Don't Bury Me • John Prine. WB Music Corp. o/b/o Walden Music (BMI).

Sabu Visits The Twin Cities Alone • John Prine. Bruised Oranges (Admin. by Wixen Music Publishing Inc.) (ASCAP).

Saddle In The Rain • John Prine. WB Music Corp. o/b/o Walden Music (BMI).

Sam Stone • John Prine. WB Music Corp. o/b/o Walden Music (BMI).

She Is My Everything • John Prine. TommyJack Music (BMI).

Six O'Clock News • John Prine. WB Music Corp. o/b/o Walden Music (BMI).

Sleepy Eyed Boy • John Prine. Bruised Oranges (Admin. by Wixen Music Publishing Inc.) (ASCAP).

Somewhere Someone's Falling In Love • John Prine; Donnie Fritts. Bruised Oranges (Admin. by Wixen Music Publishing Inc.) (ASCAP); Donnie Fritts Music (BMI).

Souvenirs • John Prine. WB Music Corp. o/b/o Walden Music (BMI).

Space Monkey • John Prine; Peter Case. Weona Music (Admin. by Wixen Music Publishing Inc.) (BMI); Trumpet Blast Music (BMI).

Spanish Pipedream • John Prine. WB Music Corp. o/b/o Walden Music (BMI).

Speed Of The Sound Of Loneliness • John Prine. Bruised Oranges (Admin. by Wixen Music Publishing Inc.) (ASCAP).

Storm Windows • John Prine. Bruised Oranges (Admin. by Wixen Music Publishing Inc.) (ASCAP).

Sweet Revenge • John Prine. WB Music Corp. o/b/o Walden Music (BMI).

Taking A Walk • John Prine; Pat McLaughlin. TommyJack Muisc (BMI); Corn Country Music (BMI).

That's The Way The World Goes 'Round • John Prine. Bruised Oranges (Admin. by Wixen Music Publishing Inc.) (ASCAP).

The Bottomless Lake • John Prine. Bruised Oranges (Admin. by Wixen Music Publishing Inc.) (ASCAP).

The Great Compromise • John Prine. WB Music Corp. o/b/o Walden Music (BMI).

The Late John Garfield Blues • John Prine. WB Music Corp. o/b/o Walden Music (BMI).

The Oldest Baby In The World • John Prine; Donnie Fritts. Bruised Oranges (Admin. by Wixen Music Publishing Inc.) (ASCAP); Donnie Fritts Music (BMI).

The Sins Of Memphisto • John Prine. Weona Music (Admin. by Wixen Music Publishing Inc.) (BMI).

There She Goes • John Prine. Bruised Oranges (Admin. by Wixen Music Publishing Inc.) (ASCAP).

Unwed Fathers • John Prine; Bobby Braddock. Bruised Oranges (Admin. by Wixen Music Publishing Inc.) (ASCAP); Sony/ATV Tree Publishing (BMI).

Way Back Then • John Prine. Weona Music (Admin. by Wixen Music Publishing Inc.) (BMI).

Yes I Guess They Oughta Name A Drink After You • John Prine. WB Music Corp. o/b/o Walden Music (BMI).

You Got Gold • John Prine; Keith Sykes. Weona Music (Admin. by Wixen Music Publishing Inc.) (BMI); Keith Sykes Music (BMI).

Your Flag Decal Won't Get You Into Heaven Anymore • John Prine. WB Music Corp. o/b/o Walden Music (BMI).

IMAGE CREDITS

Front Cover • John Prine at Atlantic Records Studio during sessions for Diamonds in the Rough, New York City, 1972.

Dedication • Al Bunetta photo courtesy of Ed Feeney.

Credits • Typical setup of John Prine stage.

Forward • From right to left: John Prine with his brother Billy, and cousin Charles Allen, posing on the steps of the abandoned old prison down by Airdrie Hill.

Inside Photo • Postcard of Main Street in Paradise, KY.

Aimless Love • John Prine on stage with Kris Kristofferson and Garry Fish. Photo courtesy of Garry Fish.

Ain't Hurtin' Nobody • Front/back of John's lesson record card from the Old Town School of Folk Music.

Inside Photo • From left to right: John Prine, Harry Waller, Stephen Wade and Steve Goodman on ferry boat to Mariposa Folk Festival in Toronto, ON.

All The Best • Album notes written by John Prine for the album The Missing Years.

Inside Photo • Bonnie Raitt, John Prine and Steve Goodman performing on stage.

Angel From Montgomery • Left – Dave Prine playing the violin. / Right – Handwritten song lyrics by John Prine.

Automobile • John Prine leaning on car.

Blue Umbrella • Left – Handwritten song lyrics by John Prine. / Right – Steve Goodman and John Prine performing on stage.

Inside Photo • John Prine performing on stage.

Bruised Orange (Chain Of Sorrow) • Handwritten song lyrics by John Prine.

Christmas In Prison • Newspaper article written by John Segraves from Washington Star-News, Washington, DC, November 9, 1972.

Common Sense • Left – John Prine and Al Bunetta in June 1972. / Right – Al Bunetta and John Prine in the studio.

Inside Photo • The marquee from the John Prine performance at Orpheum Theatre, Los Angeles, CA, June 10, 2011. Photo by Julie Blore-Bizot.

Crazy As A Loon • Left – John Prine at kitchen table in 1973. / Right – John Prine in recording studio in 2003. Courtesy of Dave Jacques.

Crooked Piece Of Time • Left – John Prine standing with guitar. Photo by Hope Powell. / Right – John Prine photo shoot by Jim Shea.

Daddy's Little Pumpkin • Left – Mema and Grandpa Prine. / Right – Handwritten lyrics by John Prine.

Dear Abby • "Dear Abby" newspaper article referencing John Prine's song from 1985.

Donald And Lydia • John Prine performing on stage.

Inside Photo • John Prine performing on stage at Chicago Theatre, Chicago, IL, February 8, 2008.

From left to right: Jason Wilber, John Prine, Mary Gauthier, Iris DeMent, Dave Jacques. Photo by Jamie Gannon.

Everything Is Cool • Multi-instrumentalist Phil Parlapiano, John Prine and guitarist Bill Bonk sharing the microphone on stage. Photo by Maria Camillo.

Far From Me • Typewritten song lyrics with handwriting edits by John Prine.

Fish And Whistle • Left – John Prine catches a fish, September 1976. / Right – Bill Prine, John's father, posing with a fish.

Inside Photo • Skip's Drive-In restaurant in Maywood, IL.

Glory Of True Love • Left – Verna and Bill Prine, John's parents. Courtesy of Doug Prine. / Right – Idell and E.S. Prine, John's grandparents, February 1951.

Grandpa Was A Carpenter • Left – John's father by an old shack. / Right – Grandfather Prine seated in a chair.

Inside Photo • The marquee from the John Prine performance at Rialto Square Theatre, Joliet, IL, March 4, 2010. Photo by Jamie Gannon.

Hello In There • Left – John Prine at the Old Town School of Folk Music, Chicago, IL. / Right – John Prine on stage at the Fifth Peg, Chicago, IL in 1970.

How Lucky • Candids of John Prine in the studio with legendary producer Sam Phillips, Rachel Peer Prine, Jerry Phillips, Al Bunetta, and Knox Phillips.

I Just Want To Dance With You • John Prine performing on stage at "A Tribute To Steve Goodman" at Arie Crown Theater, Chicago, IL, January 26, 1985.

Inside Photo • John Prine playing pool in New York, April 1974. Photo by Peter Cunningham.

In Spite Of Ourselves • John Prine and Iris Dement recording at Jack's Tracks in Nashville, TN, January 20, 2016. Photo by Amy Richmond.

It's A Big Old Goofy World • Handwritten song lyrics by John Prine.

Jesus The Missing Year • Handwritten song lyrics by John Prine.

Lake Marie • John Prine adjusts his tie while stationed in Germany, 1966.

Let's Talk Dirty In Hawaiian • Cover art for the 7-inch vinyl single of Let's Talk Dirty In Hawaiian / Kokomo.

Inside Photo • John Prine with his one-time backing band, The Famous Potatoes. From left to right: Howard Levy, Johnny Burns, Tommy Piekarski, John Prine.

Linda Goes To Mars • John Prine with guitar promotional photo.

Living In The Future • Handwritten song lyrics by John Prine.

Long Monday • John Prine walking down a road in Ireland. Front cover photo from the album Fair & Square. Photo by Nutan.

Love, Love, Love • The Prine Brothers (Dave, John, Billy and Doug) on stage at Proviso East High School, Maywood, IL, May 15, 2010. Photo by Paul Natkin.

Maureen, Maureen • Handwritten song lyrics by John Prine.

Mexican Home • Upper Left – John's father Bill on Dewey Lake in 1965. / Lower Left – John's father Bill at center, with Uncle June and Jimmy Polsgrove-Photo courtesy of Doug Prine. / Upper Middle - John's father Bill, brother Doug, John and brother Billy posing in 1965. / Lower Middle – John's father Bill cleaning snow off the family Buick in Maywood, IL, January 26, 1967. / Right – John Prine songwriting with his guitar in Crosslake, MN, September 1976.

One Red Rose • John Prine and Steve Goodman seated at dinner.

Only Love • The Prine Brothers (John, Doug, Billy and Dave) seated on a couch.

Inside Photo • The general store in Paradise, KY.

Paradise • John Prine's Grandaddy Ham (seated) and Bubby Short at the Green River, Muhlenberg County, KY.

Inside Photo • The world's largest shovel from the Peabody Coal Company.

People Puttin' People Down • John Prine, Garry Fish and Jerry Douglas perform in CA. Photo courtesy of by Garry Fish.

Picture Show • Handwritten song lyrics by John Prine.

Please Don't Bury Me • Handwritten song lyrics by John Prine.

Sabu Visits The Twin Cities Alone • Above – John Prine standing on a street, June 1979. / Below - Handwritten song lyrics by John Prine.

Saddle In The Rain • Left - Handwritten song lyrics by John Prine. / Right – Dave Prine and John Prine performing on stage. Photo courtesy of Dave Prine.

Inside Photo • From left to right: Rick Schulman, Jerry McEwen, Al Bunetta, John Prine, Charles Cochran, Cowboy Jack Clement, Dave Prine.

Sam Stone • John Prine in Army uniform.

She Is My Everything • Left – John and Fiona Prine photo used in the packaging for the album The Missing Years. / Right – Fiona and John Prine walking down the street. Photos by Jim McGuire.

Six O'Clock News • Left – handwritten song lyrics by John Prine. / Right – John Prine seated with guitar in Memphis, TN in 1971.

Sleepy Eyed Boy • John Prine singing alongside Steve Goodman on stage.

Somewhere Someone's Falling In Love • John and his brother Billy Prine looking at an electric guitar.

Souvenirs • Upper Left – From left to right: Earl Pionke, John Prine, Jimmy Buffett, Nancy Goodman-Tenney, Jessie Goodman, Steve Goodman, Fred Holstein, Eddie Holstein. / Lower Left – Steve Goodman gifts John Prine a Wurlitzer jukebox. / Right – Steve Goodman, longtime manager Al Bunetta and John Prine posing. Photo by David Gahr.

Space Monkey • Handwritten song lyrics by John Prine.

Spanish Pipedream • Tom Waits, Bonnie Raitt and John Prine backstage at Grand Ole Opry, Nashville, TN in 1975.

Speed Of The Sound Of Loneliness • Left – John Prine and Nanci Griffith Wings Of Desire tour poster. / Right – Guitarist Jason Wilber, John Prine and bassist Dave Jacques in 2009.

Inside Photo • John Prine on stage at Proviso East High School, Maywood, IL, May 15, 2010. Photo by Paul Natkin.

Storm Windows • 1110 South First Avenue in Maywood, IL, where John grew up, covered with snow, January 26, 1967.

Sweet Revenge • Newspaper article advertising "Tom Prine" from November 1971.

Taking A Walk • Left – John Prine promotional photo shoot, Nashville, TN, December 4, 2009. Photo by Jim Shea. / Right – John Prine recording at Jack's Tracks, Nashville, TN, January 2016. Photo by Amy Richmond.

That's The Way The World Goes 'Round • Left – Girls hired by Asylum Records to dress up as bruised oranges pose with record store personnel at a record store in Norfolk, VA, July 28, 1978. / Right – Steve Goodman, John Prine, and Johnny Burns on stage.

The Bottomless Lake • John's youngest brother Billy seated on a boat dock.

Inside Photo • John Prine promotional photo shoot with guitar, Nashville, TN, December 4, 2009. Photo by Jim Shea.

Inside Photo • Typewritten musings by John Prine.

The Great Compromise • Kris Kristofferson speaking with John Prine at the Troubadour, Los Angeles, CA in 1972.

The Late John Garfield Blues • Handwritten song lyrics by John Prine.

The Oldest Baby In The World • Left - Outside the original Muscle Shoals Sound Studio at 3614 Jackson Highway, Muscle Shoals, AL. From left to right: Tony Joe White, Donnie Fritts, Kris Kristofferson, Jerry Wexler, John Prine, Dan Penn. / Right - Donnie Fritts and John Prine.

The Sins Of Memphisto • Handwritten song lyrics by John Prine.

There She Goes • Handwritten song lyrics by John Prine.

Unwed Fathers • Left – John Prine performing on stage in 1974. Photo by Dick Cooper. / Right - Handwritten song lyrics by John Prine.

Inside Photo • John Prine performing on stage.

Way Back Then • John playing guitar while stationed with the Army in Germany.

Yes I Guess They Oughta Name A Drink After You • John Prine relaxing on a couch.

You Got Gold • Father Bill Prine at age 18, and mother Verna at age 14. Photo courtesy of by Doug Prine.

Your Flag Decal Won't Get You Into Heaven Anymore • Newspaper article written by Robert Martin.

Inside Photo • John Prine on pommel horse for Proviso East High School, Maywood, IL.

Back Cover • John Prine promotional photo, Nashville, TN, December 4, 2009. Photo by Jim Shea.

Except where noted, all images are from the John Prine Family private collection.